CONTENTS

By The Crumbling Wall: Berlin Notes
Kaiser Haq

I

Vive L'Anarchie was still brazenly scrawled at the top of the Brandenburg Gate, a high-water mark left by the November tidal wave. Tourists trampled gaily past, indifferent to the tergiversations of weather, cameras and camcorders busy. The paths along the Wall were trampled to mud. Four months ago a photojournalist doing Berlin would have had to wait to catch the solitary stroller to provide poignant focus to his pictures. The grim wall and its intimidating guards have been translated into Disneyland creations. Simulacra, in Baudrillard's sense of signs that no longer signify. A guard strutting the circular rampart in front of the gate lent a hand to a small boy, hauled him up to be photographed, then gently helped him down. The more agile adults scaled the Wall and posed for their companions. At the many holes in the Wall guards appeared and stood still while cameras clicked and camcorders purred - a favourite shot. Along the tourist track chips of the Wall were being sold by vendors who displayed their collections on mats and trestle tables. Prices depended on size and whether there was any graffitti. A chip of the first water - fist-sized, with an interesting bit of graffitti - might fetch, even after haggling, the price of a good meal. Adventurous tourists came armed with pick, adze or hammer to quarry pieces for themselves. The more enterprising Wall merchants trucked away mounds of chips for export to America and Japan. Since the material of the Wall seems no different from any other concrete there may well be fakes on the market. One can imagine a sideline for structural engineers who might be called upon to pronounce on dubious chips. Already vendors worried by dwindling graffitti reserves had invested in spray cans which they urged on passing tourists to use as they pleased on the Wall: *Amusieren Sie! Machen Sie Graffitti!* I'd gone resolved to bring back a few chips myself, but carnivalesque commercialisation of a historic symbol made me give up the idea.

2

I was on a Goethe Institute package tour. First eight weeks doing the Institute's beginners' German course in a city of my choice, then a week to visit two other cities. The package had been designed to give a taste of Germany to interested foreigners active in their native cultural arenas. Berlin, on account of the Crumbling Wall, was an instant choice for the eight-week stint, but generally I was glad to be in the land that had produced some of my favourite writers and given me my name. I went with hopes of picking up enough German to justify it. Overambitious, I picked up just a little, *ein Bischen*, barely enough to be able to explain how I got it. I'd been named by a Granduncle taken with Kaiser Bill out of anti-British sentiment. (Yet in an odd way he was an Anglophile, as his grandnephew has turned out to be.) But he mightn't have thought of the German Emperor if 'Kaiser', pronounced with 's' as an unvoiced alveolar fricative, wasn't an Indian word of the same import. That makes it, perhaps, a case of overdetermination.

Of German writers Nietzche had lately been much in my thoughts, particularly in connection with western Europe's move to leave behind the limiting ideology of nationalism, which it had created two centuries back and exported to the rest of the world. Europe seemed to be fulfilling a prophecy in 'The Wanderer and Its Shadow' that 'the people . . . will assail the capitalists, the merchants and the princes of the stock exchange with a progressive tax and slowly create in fact a middle class which will be in a position to *forget* socialism like an illness it has recovered from. The practical outcome of this spreading democratisation will first of all be a European League of Nations within which each individual nation . . . will possess the status and rights of a canton.' He suggests a solution to the problems of labour that the West seems to have adopted: 'That which we now call justice . . . does not pay regard only to the moment or exploit opportunities as they occur but reflects on the enduring advantage of all conditions and classes and therefore also keeps in mind the wellbeing of the worker, his contentment of body and soul - *so that* he and his posterity shall work well for our posterity too and be relied on for a longer span of time than a single human life. The *exploitation* of the worker was, it has now been realised, a piece of stupidity, an exhausting of the soil at the expense of the future, an imperilling of society.' He offers the vision of a new universalism, exhorting his readers 'To write better . . . to think better; continually to invent things more worth communicating and to be able actually to communicate them; to become translatable into the language of one's neighbour; to make ourselves accessible to the understanding of those foreigners who learn our language; to assist towards making all good things common property and freely available to the free-minded; finally, to *prepare the way* for that still-distant state of things in which the good Europeans will come into possession of their great task: the direction and supervision of the total culture of the earth.'

Sorry for the long quotes, but it would be futile to try to give a summary, so pithy is Nietzche's style, so significant the ideas. Even the Soviet initiative in demilitarisation is anticipated, albeit a trifle hyperbolically: '. . . there will come a great day on which a nation distinguished for wars and victories and for the highest development of military discipline and thinking . . . will cry of its own free will: "*we shall shatter the sword*" - and demolish its entire military machine. *To disarm while being the best armed*, out of an *elevation* of sensibility - that is the means to *real* peace.' And now, complicating matters, in the wake of *glasnost* and *perestroika*, had appeared nationalist revivals.

3

Germany, I quipped soon after arrival, is overdisciplined. Everything had to follow a systematic procedure, deviations were not to be tolerated. I was billeted in a three-room flat which I shared with Mahmat, a 19-year-old Istanbul University student, and Tadeyuki, a 26-year-old journalism graduate from Tokyo. On registration day I followed Mahmat into a bus and put down my fare beside him. The driver snapped it up with a growl and handed it back, accompanying the gesture with a furious remonstrance whose import one could decipher without any German: fares had to be paid one at a time! Though a good four inches separated my money from Mahmat's its sight must have been an annoying distraction.

Since Germans pride themselves on their discipline and efficiency it was galling to them to find themselves bested in these respects. *'Sind die Deutschen faul?'* (Are Germans lazy?) my textbook asked, then compared their periods of work, holiday and sick leave with those of the Japanese.

But Tadeyuki didn't seem to be a typical Japanese. He dressed in quasi-Bohemian fashion, gave the impression of being sloppy and was in fact critical of the workaholism and materialism of his compatriots. That he possessed a hard core of Japanese discipline - besides working at German he spend an hour a day on Polish, Russian and English - was easy to miss, and to our landlord Herr Daryush (his father was Iranian) a series of incidents cast him in the role of the odd Japanese out. All three incidents involved difficulty - Freudians please note - in opening the door.

Incident 1: Tadeyuki came home and couldn't open the door. Neither Mahmat nor I was in. He struggled in vain to put the keys in (there were three locks), then called Herr Daryush. Nothing wrong with keys or locks, just the technique of putting one into the other.

Incident 2: One of Tadeyuki's keys wouldn't fit the lock. I was in and had a go. Something definitely seemed wrong with his key - it couldn't have been the lock because it readily accomodated my key. We called Herr Daryush. He tried once, then asked for a pin. The key was of the sort that had a socket-like hole at the tip. Daryush scoured the hole with the pin and dredged out a wad of fluff. It had entered the key in Tadeyuki's pocket. Daryush had been in Japan for a week and the visit had made a lasting impression. The Japanese were the cleanest people on earth; even taxi-drivers wore spotless white gloves.

'You are not Japanese,' he said to Tadeyuki and feigned punches of exasperation.

Tadeyuki tried to mollify him with chocolates.

Herr Daryush said: 'First you can't put your key in, now you've put dirt into the key. I'm waiting for the third time.'

Incident 3: Back from his customary weekend spree in the small hours of a Saturday, Tadeyuki found he couldn't open the house door. This was more serious than the previous occasions when he had been thwarted by the door of our first-floor flat. He pressed the first-floor doorbell and when the intercom was turned on yelled in despair: 'Professor! (meaning me) I can't open the door. Please come down and open the door.'

The door opened and an irate Herr Daryush upbraided him for drinking too much.

Our flat was No 4. Herr Daryush's, also on the first floor, in No 3.

4

The Goethe Institute is on Hardenbergstrasse, which also accommodates its Anglophone rivals the British Council and USIS, and is by far the busiest of the three establishments, with classes in three shifts and a range of courses. Mine was *Grundstufe-1*, absolute beginners', and my class was in the afternoon, which, late riser that I am, suited me well. Drifting in and out of sleep I'd hear a noise like a quadruped galloping; Mahmat and Tadeyuki hurrying to catch the bus to morning classes. Mahmat, who had taken German at school, and wanted to improve his proficiency for the sake of a holiday job as a tourist guide, was in *Mittelstufe*. Tadeyuki, who wanted to specialise in Central European affairs, had previously visited Germany and Poland, but like me was in *Grundstufe-1*. Ideally, Tadeyuki and I should have been stammering in broken German under Mahmat's supervision. Instead, Mahmat and Tadeyuki practised their English on me.

I didn't mind. My resolutions to immerse myself in *Deutsch* (I hadn't taken any English writings except my own, in case anyone wanted to look at them) had begun to crack under the strain of learning German inflexions. Halfway through the ninety-minute periods I found myself struggling to keep awake. Only shots of strong mocha in the breaks kept me going. I began smoking more. Since it was forbidden to smoke inside except on special occasions like parties or a vernissage, I joined other smokers in the garden at the back or the terrace in front.

I lacked motivation. I could go through life quite happily without German. The Poles, the most diligent (and numerous) of the Institute's pupils, couldn't. They were immigrants and had been granted a 10 month stipend by the West German government to study for the language proficiency certificate without which they couldn't be considered for employment. The Turkish contingent, exchange visitors like me, took the lessons in cavalier spirit. In between were those whose careers would benefit with German, like my flatmates or students like Burzo and Darrah.

Burzo was born in Tehran, but his family, Bah'ai by faith and socialist in politics, had emigrated to America when he was a small boy. He had kept alive his family's radicalism by going on to study at the New School of Social Thought, and had taken time off to learn German so that he could read Adorno, Habermas and their like in the original.

Burzo hated The System. He thrived on his hate. He enthused over the anti-Poll Tax rallies in London, which he thought presaged social disturbances throughout the West. When a police car zoomed by in a chase he could barely contain his excitement. I thought he'd love to chuck a stone at it. He didn't like capitalist West Germany, which he described as Yuppie-land. And he disliked German 'arrogance' as much as American 'arrogance'.

Darrah thought that whatever they might feel towards others Americans couldn't feel arrogant towards Europeans - a remnant of the old American cultural inferiority complex. She was a graduate student at a mid-western university and had followed her German boyfriend to Berlin. She wanted some credits in German language and literature before getting down to a Ph D thesis on early twentieth-century British women writers. She liked it in Berlin, particularly evenings of bar-crawling and chain-smoking with her friend, and even after a very late night could look disconcertingly beautiful, especially with her hair done up.

But even Darrah found a dourness in Germans that took litres of beer to

6

dissolve. Lacking intimate experience of Germans I took due note of the comments of those who did, several married to Germans: a Polish English teacher, a Brazilian psychoanalyst, an English playwright. The emerging profile compounded dourness with xenophobia and a national superiority complex (with spouses and friends providing rule-proving exceptions).

The shyest of my fellow-students, a Polish music teacher, loosened up once on half a bottle of vodka and bewailed growing resentment against immigrants. It was worse in East Germany. The eastern side of the Wall, he said, was free of graffitti, save a few demanding *Ausländers Weg* (foreigners out). In West Berlin stickers were on sale: *Deutschland Mein Vaterland* blazoned across a map in which Germany had encroached into Poland. More comically, at an election-night party in East Berlin a tipsy reveller upbraided Darrah for smoking Benson & Hedges menthols instead of German cigarettes. I met thoughtful West Germans dismayed at the trend and unhappy over reunification because they thought an enlarged Germany might destabilise Europe. Would good Europeanism be able to contain nationalism or would Western Europe be thrown out of kilter and Eastern Europe become Balkanised?

For East Germans, citizens of closed societies for over half a century, the transition to democracy can't be without the 'strain of civilisation' (Popper's phrase). When many of them will discover that they are ill-equipped to face the competition in a capitalist society, and unemployment rises, the social atmosphere across the country is likely to suffer. In German cities today single women range freely through the night. The *U-Bahn* runs smoothly on an honour system. Cafes and *Kniepes* stay open till the small hours and the atmosphere in them, compared to, say, London pubs, is wonderfully relaxed. There's no inner-city problem. No racial violence, whatever the underlying tensions. No muggers at large. All this may change. Signs of increased neo-Nazi activity were already there. On April 20, Hitler's birthday, Tadeyuki saw celebrating skinheads skirmish with opponents in East Berlin's Alexanderplatz. The Kreuzberg Anarchists tried unsuccessfully to cross over and join the fray.

Interestingly, in tussling with nationalism, European internationalism has a potent ally in popular culture, the stuff we high-brow types deride - the mindless music, the mass-produced Hollywood films. More than the fact that almost every other person in Berlin had a bit of English I was suprised by the music in supermarkets - all English pop songs. In cinemas and on TV 98% of films are American.

A popular German TV show, 'Tutti Frutti', combines titillation and fanfare for the EEC. A bevy of attractive girls representing the EEC countries appear in swimsuits while two competitors, a man and a woman, vie with each other in guessing games. Points earned obtain for all the pleasure of watching one of the girls strip - chastely, down to G-string only. Surplus points at the end are converted into cash. If either competitor loses he or she must 'pay' by stripping. Punctuating the show the EEC girls cavort and sing, with two refrains: 'Super super Europe 1992', and - apparently nonsense - 'Chin-chin'. The first time we watched the show Tadeyuki rolled on the floor with laughter. 'Chin-chin' is Japanese for 'prick'.

I wanted to meet Günter Grass, and Peter Schneider, both Berliners. The phone book had only one Gunter Grass, a dentist, and a string of Peter Schneiders. I sought the Institute's help to track them down. But Grass was travelling and though his secretary forwarded a piece I'd written in connection with his Bangladesh visit in 1986 (*London Magazine*, Apr/May 1989) he didn't respond. Schneider was down with a bug ('Berlin flu - it just refuses to go away') but promised an appointment as soon as he got well.

I'd discovered Schneider in America when his splendid Berlin novel *Die Mauerspringer* appeared in English as *The Wall Jumper*. I also came across a short piece translated in *The New York Times Book Review* in which he advocated the hyrbrid 'essay-novel'. It interested me because it seemed to offer a good alternative to the cliches of magic realism. It seemed fitting that there should be a dialectic between the two modern forms: Montaigne and Cervantes, we may recall, were contemporaries. So far the interaction has been in the direction of novel incorporating essay. I toyed with the idea of essays that would subsume fiction: possibilities seemed endless.

I went a little early to my appointment at Schneider's flat off Kurfürstendamm. He came in a little late. His charming wife let me in and, when I declined an invitation to watch TV, left me to browse and watch their two children go through their pre-bedtime cavorting. I discovered an essay by Schneider in a New Directions anthology from the mid-70s; an impassioned critique of capitalist Germany where people didn't touch except to exchange blows, where everyone was expected to go about in sourfaced pursuit of money, etc.

Schneider walked in, casually dressed in jeans and jacket and looking much younger than his fifty years. I thought he could have become an actor instead of writing films: his 'Knife in the Head' has won critical acclaim. His smile was shy and frank at the same time. He apologised for being late; he'd been detained by his Swedish publisher who was visiting Berlin and wanted to hear his views on the ongoing changes: Schneider, a close friend of Rudi Dutschke, writes political essays regularly.

We settled at a round table. Schneider fetched a bottle of white wine and two glasses. We drank, talked, chain-smoked for over two hours, interrupted only by phone calls. Once he spoke in Italian; it seemed as good as his English. We started with literature but soon turned to changing Germany and the changes it had brought about in Schneider's way of thinking. Even a year back he'd dismiss much of the criticism of East Germany as exaggerated. Now he saw it was much worse there. Children had been taught to accord admiring recognition to portraits of Honecker by the time they finished toilet-training. East Germans were not only poorer but deprived even in health care, one area in which even their critics thought socialism had worked wonders. More shockingly, there was a peculiarly 'innocent' racism. The official line, that socialism unburdened East Germany of any guilt over the Nazi past, engendered a holier-than-thou attitude that blinded East Germany to their own racism towards Poles and Vietnamese. Vietnam had agreed a novel method of paying back war loans. Thousands of Vietnamese were sent to East Germany where, after surrendering passports, they were quartered in barracks and provided employment. Nearly half their earnings had to be surrendered to settle the national debt. East Germans complained that they were taking away their jobs, their women.

Schneider thought, rightly, that Germans ought to accept the fact that like many others in Europe theirs was a multi-cultural society. This was quite evident in West Berlin where doner kebab shops are as common as Indian restaurants in the UK, and there are two Turkish cable TV channels, on one of which I watched a delightful send-up of the debauchery of sheikhs. Foreigners in Germany, besides Turks and East Europeans, also include a floating population on political asylum. I heard that as many as a hundred Indian asylum-seekers were entering Berlin every day. Till they got official assistance, they kipped down in the zoo, which at midnight looked like the platform of an Indian railway station. Employers looking for cheap part-time labour were sure of finding bargains here. It was a precarious existence, vulnerable to sudden reversals. Those who'd come claiming persecution by Rajiv's Congress government were now being rounded up for deportation.

The final collapse of socialism in practice had opened Schneider's eyes to flaws in his theories as well. For instance, the demand for the sacrifice of self-interest to the collective good no longer seemed compatible with 'human nature': why should he write if not for individual recognition? I couldn't help pontificating at this point; 'The thinker for our times is Nietzsche, not Marx. We'd do well to remember two prerequisites for human greatness that he discovered in the ancient Greeks: *askesis*, self-overcoming, and the *agon*, individual competition! But disillusionment with radicalism didn't mean that earlier criticism of capitalist society was invalid, only that the solutions had to be sought democratically. One ought to be sceptical of apocalyptic answers.' I mentioned Popper. He said he'd referred to Popper in an essay, suggesting that the Popperian theory of 'falsifiability', an attempt to systematise the trial-and-error methods of science, could also be used in dealing with social ideas.

Guilt over the Nazi past was a central preoccupation in the work of Schneider and other West German writers of his generation. I wondered if abandoned radicalism would provide another burden of guilt to deal with.

Schneider asked me about my own politics. In earlier years I'd fellow-travelled with factions inspired by the insurrectionary Maoism of the Indian Naxalites; then in the state of anomie following the Bangladesh independence war, in which I fought, I became gradually deradicalised. The final break was prompted by events in Cambodia. When I went to Britain in 1978 on a Commonwealth scholarship, Leftist friends in London, leading a sort of 'Magic Mountain' existence, talked of getting hold of Khieu Samphan's PhD thesis in economics (University of Paris?) in the hope that it would reveal a *sutra* that could be used to repeat the Cambodian revolution in Bangladesh. Then, to everyone's embarrassment, the horror-stories came out.

Our conversation ended on a question. Schneider said that he knew what to think about Europe - the desirability of an open society etc - but what about the non-western world? He didn't know enough to form opinions but couldn't show unconcern either. At least not after his friend, the semiotician Tzvetan Todorov, pointed out the consequences. The problem relates to universals: are there any universal values or not? If not, if everything is relative, one would have to accept female circumcision in Sudan, *sati* in India, even the Nazi atrocities. And if one didn't subscribe to such absurd relativism it would be difficult to accept the claims of tinpot dictators that the unique socio-cultural conditions in their countries demanded military rule or a one-party system.

6

Two days later Schneider was to give his first reading in East Berlin. My German was still virtually non-existent, but I decided to go and try to soak in the atmosphere. It was my first visit to East Berlin. I took the *S-Bahn* to Friedrichstrasse and, map in hand, sought out the Jewish Community Centre where the reading would be held. I still had nearly an hour in hand and felt like a drink. Eating and drinking places weren't as common as in West Berlin and I passed a few that had shut early. At the *Tanz-Cafe* I eventually entered I had to wait over a quarter of an hour for a beer, though the place was more than half-empty.

Schneider read for an hour and the discussion lasted twice as long. All the anxious questions raised by the impending reunification came up. I hurried back, for the checkpoint closed at midnight - and ran into trouble.

East Germany forbade the bringing in, or taking out, of her currency. Visitors were supposed to exchange money at East German banks where the two Marks were at par. Outside the *Zoologisches Garten*, West Germany's main railway station, currency racketeers by the dozen flashed East German Marks, which they exchanged at 5:1 against the Deutschmark. Like everybody else, I made use of the offer, exchanging DM10 for 50 Ostmarks. Warned that there might be random checks I carried the money, unchallenged, inside a packet of chewing gum. After paying for the beer and a packet of awful cigarettes I had over 40 marks left. In the excitement of the literary evening I neglected to conceal them.

A boyish customs officer beckoned me to one side and handed me a currency declaration form, where there were separate columns for Deutschmarks, other foreign currencies, and Ostmarks. I tried a ploy. I took out the East German coins which came to a few Marks and a few pfennigs, and declared them, hoping this show of honesty would satisfy my inquisitor, and since a few coins could hardly count as 'currency' I'd be let through. I was wrong. He ushered me into a side room and ordered me to empty the contents of my pockets onto a table and turn the pockets inside out.

As I placed the incriminating banknotes on the table I had nightmare visions of being locked up, tried and fined, perhaps even sentenced to jail.

An explanation was demanded. I said I'd borrowed the money from a friend in West Berlin who had probably got them from an East German bank.

I decided to throw myself on the official's mercy.

'I'm sorry,' I said, 'really sorry.'

He was mollified. The amount involved was a trifle. It was enough that he had proved himself in his job.

'I am a customs officer,' he said.

I said: 'A very good one.'

He said: 'Go and deposit all DDR currency in the bank. Then you can go.'

Which meant that I could come again and blow the money - and I did, on coffee and cakes, beer, a substantial meal and a couple of packets of Marlboro. To visitors from the West, things were cheap in East Berlin and with the 5:1 unofficial rate of exchange it was like getting things free: one pleasure tourists will miss after reunification.

As I was leaving the search-room my Customs Officer picked up a West German coin from the floor and handed it to me. I protested it wasn't mine.

'Keep it. Use it for telephone.'

Enriched by 10 pfennigs I returned to West Berlin.

7

Schneider had said he'd like to talk with me more about Third World matters, but became so busy that it was impossible, even though we did meet again to celebrate his fiftieth birthday, a pleasant evening enlivened by two itinerant American jazz performers. But the subject came up in my conversations with David Spencer, from Halifax, Yorkshire. He came to our class a few days late, having demoted himself from one slightly higher because he couldn't keep up. When, in answer to our *Lehrer*'s introductory queries he said that he worked in theatre, I took him for an actor. With his seemingly careless attire and hair with lower edges close-cropped all round, he seemed to fit the role. Quite by chance I discovered that he was a playwright. We started talking. We swapped our writings.

A Verity Bargate winner, David's plays were in dialect, about working class life, and steeped in Arthur Miller-ish bleakness. His wife was German and they'd decided to live in Berlin because its social security system was better than anywhere in Britain. He was writing a film, on contract, besides selling occasional ideas to TV. He had picked up enough German to get around but felt he needed to bone up on grammar in order to learn the language well.

David was saddened by the failure of the socialist experiment in Europe but believed the dialectics of exploiter and exploited still remained to be played out in a global context. This is mere wishful thinking of course. The global proletariat of Third Worldism is a fiction that can no longer be sustained. With the take-off in the Pacific rim and the oil boom in the middle-east and elsewhere, and at the other end of the scale the emergence of LDCs (Least Developed Countries) as bottomless receptacles for aid, the charge of exploitation looked like no more than an expression of *ressentiment*, in the Nietzschean sense.

David branded me a 'Third World Tory', whatever that may mean, but kept an open mind and, I believe, took my points seriously. And for my part I felt a corresponding sympathy for his predicament. His playwriting had removed him from the working class he wrote about. They weren't his audience. Those among whom he felt an alien - middle-class writers and intellectuals - had accorded him the recognition a writer needs. So the notion of a socialist future, when serious art would return to the people, naturally appealed to him as the answer to his double alienation.

If this is idealism it was leavened by an impish cynicism. He loved to take the mickey out of Burzo, who referred to him admiringly as 'the English Anarchist'.

Burzo reported gleefully that the Scots had declared that the Thatcher government had no mandate in Scotland, where her party was in the minority.

David: 'She has her mandate by virtue of the drubbing the English gave the Scots centuries back.' (This, I ought to add, is a stodgy paraphrase. I forget David's exact words.)

This was doubly hilarious to those who knew that David was of Irish parentage and had often gone on 'Troops Out' marches.

Burzo said something about the 'phoney nature' of the current US-Soviet amity.

David: 'Nothing phoney about it. Now's our chance to gang up with the Russians and kick the shit out of the Chinese.'

8

Just before I left Berlin David asked me to dinner and, Madhur Jaffrey open on a book-rest, cooked a passable tandoori. The conversation drifted long into the night and finally became entangled over the question of whether or not the sophisticated surveillance provided by hi-tech were going to bring in a police state. An anarchist couple thought this had very nearly happened already. David took the moderate view that one oughtn't to forget that such surveillance helped assure the safety of the ordinary citizen. I thought it all depended on the strength of the institutions that safeguarded individual liberty. The anarchist proclivity to attack all institutions seemed to increase the risks of police states developing.

What happened where there was no sophisticated surveillance, where the 'knowledge/power' network (a useful notion introduced by Foucault) was primitive? In Bangladesh for instance? Fourteen years back my youngest brother left home for college, where he had to deposit the fee for his final pre-university examination. He didn't go to the college; he didn't return home. He simply disappeared. He had done it twice previously, once to visit Sylhet, of whose picturesque hills he had heard much, the second time to go on a long march called by a Leftist Front. This time he didn't come back. He was an introvert. Did he, unknown to us, become fired with revolutionary zeal and join one of the insurrectionary parties then so active? Or did he simply go in search of a new life elsewhere? Is he alive or dead? The question still haunts my family.

I put it to my mildly inebriated acquaintances if it was better to have a society where technology provided near-faultless means of surveillance but where there existed democratic institutions designed to protect individual rights and, like technology, capable of endless refinement, or one that was so badly organised that people might disappear without leaving a trace?

I had no doubts about the answer.

Kaiser Haq

James Berry

POCKETLESS

In this recurring dream I have
I walk with new faces
forming behind - contoured in stages

With a heart water-clear
I mirror dream roads
and landscapes of people waving

My body pocketless like a treetrunk
my hands open as leaves
no fear of loss comes

Washed with herbal light
scales of sun pieces dress me
and change like husks

From different immunities
I collect emotions
turned colours or sounds

From wanting all
my indestructibility
I gather up myself

RELUCTANCE AND PERSUASION

Sun-eye returns because it sees
oceans of heads amassed with a terror
like alien soldiers marshalled
or strict enclosures of weaponry
full of bodies-mangling
or simply death-stench under cover.

Night shows up on and on
spreading everybody's cool
in shadow-touch, to persuade
a transfer of relaxed safety from sleep
into wakefulness.

Over and over noon comes back
scattering dazzle
in dream roads being cut
that with trips people may come
to see their other sides
and the outlook they keep.

Returning sun-eye sees
people-coldness overwhelms
more than a freezing season.

HAIKU IMPULSE

1

Fallen leaves scare him,
yet out he strolls under trees -
does autumn test him?

2

They were white, under
stones - downy stems, downy leaves,
to be green in sunlight.

3

Skin of devil-stock
by minds, he faces faces -
how does time work him?

HAPPY GOODBYE SONG

You staring summer days and shut-eye nights
on beaten places and dried-up tenants
all people awaiting no-help

eye of burner sun
watcher of stone meeting gun
impartial colluder
    with your silent walk banish pain

You burner sun you wrinkler
gripping me into a goner
having me rotting under dazzle

watching me nakedly pocketless
watching me wretchedly moneyless
watching me non-weapon loser
    with your silent walk banish pain

Now you hangers-on old ways
invasion of pain desires
people-devouring fires
lacks in varied uniform

rage of need lashing
bodies tasselled crying
all brains blunted
    wave goodbye
        saying you're spent

Now you hangers-on old ways
hidden jaws of hunger
eaters of victims beyond wonder
feeders on girls and boys out of life

glass-walled abundance taunting my worth
drills that have me establish what I loathe
all badnews no-answers all-mystery
    wave goodbye
        saying you're spent

You disordered force of the dispossessed
the convenience for death and stress
losers who fight generations later
    come equal now
        saying hello hello hello

COCONUT HUSKERS

Palm trees spread everywhere for sun.
Palm trees give nuts the sun made.

Steady steady, rhythm drives
worked knees and arms well teamed.

Bare limbs let loose down-rush, where
bare shoulders force husk onto blade.

All rises and dips hurrying up,
black bodies ripple with muscles.

All hot rub-up of work, men's
bent-back thrusts wet them like oil.

Edges of steel-hoes fly and fly
into package the elements made.

This way that way men push
and wrench powerfully.

At each third break of husk,
gold fibres cry.

Never willing to let go,
packed strings of coir say 'Whai!'

Hand-grasps take nuts
like heads at birth.

In a tree's big shadow
coconuts pile up and up.

Tossed out into the sun,
husks pile higher higher and wider.

A SCHOOLED FATHERHOOD

There in my small-boy years that day
I couldn't believe the shock,
the blow that undid me, seeing him
reduced, suddenly. Helpless, without honour
without respect, he stood indistinct
in the abuse of a white child
in the parents' look-away, don't-care faces.
Lost there, in a peculiar smile - being
an error, a denial of the man I copied,
that big-big man I'm one day to be - he made
a black history I didn't know swamp me,
hurt me, like terror-hands of a dreaded ghost.

Two men apart, from now - with him
not able to see, not able
to keep pace with time or know
my secret eye watchful -
I began to see
educated voices charging his guts
like invisible pellets of a gun
imbedding in him, daytime, nighttime.
And soon, he clean forgot
who he was. Then with his roots
and person's rights wiped away
he knew he'd known nothing always.
His deep man-structure dismantled,
a tamed dog came in him and gave him face
gave him readiness for his job -
delivering shot birds between his teeth
to get a patting beside high boots -
   my father
      my first lord
         my inviolable king.

James Berry

A World of Writers
Angus Calder

There is a tale to be told about how 'Writing Together' was hammered together, how nails dropped out as public funds were promised but not quickly forthcoming, how some exciting ideas proved to be over-ambitious and others came to sudden fruition out of sheer improvisation. It was always going to be difficult: no clear precedents in Glasgow, and the whole shebang has probably no precedent anywhere. But I can foresee that the final, biggest phase in September 1990 will involve more schools, more ethnic minority groups and more local writers' groups in events - discussions, workshops, readings, bringing together published writers from other countries with writers from Scotland - than participated in the earlier phases: the short September 1989 'trailer' and the series of events in April 1990.

The themes of language, race, class, gender, nationality and culture have been seen by the organisers as common to Scotland and the rest of the world. I've learnt that inviting writers to take part in systematic discussion of these issues may not be the best way to get them ventilated. If you combine, as *Writing Together* has done, Scottish, 'Commonwealth', African, Asian, Caribbean, Black British and European writers the lessons arise automatically. I make few claims for my own creativity, but am proud of my conception of the 'Rum and Scotch' reading first attempted at the Commonwealth Writers' Conference in Edinburgh in 1986. Get good Carribean poets together with Scottish poets in our three languages. Add a bit of Scottish music. Listen as similarities between cultures related to but resistant to Metropolitan English display themselves delightfully. The point makes itself: Caribbean 'nation language' is in origins and aurally different from Scots or Gaelic, but its use in cultural struggle is not so dissimilar. There's a tape of Whistlebinkies combining with John Agard in 1986, but alas not of the 'fusion' achieved by Agard and Aonghas MacNeacail next day and repeated at the 1987 Edinburgh Book Festival.

In April we planned a Mushaira - a type of poetry reading from the Indian sub-continent - but the date clashed with the Muslim Ramadan. So we improvised an 'Asian-Irish' night where Nuala Ní Dhomnaill read poetry in Gaelic, there was fine Sikh singing, Scottish folk cello from Ron Shaw, angry young verse from Saquib Dishmukh, reared in England, who raps in English and Urdu, and finally Irish music and dancing. The cumulative effect - one of fusion of feeling - was unpredictably magical. All the so-called Indo-European languages, spoken from Donegal to BanglaDesh, are said to derive from one originating in the Volga basin five thousand years ago . . .

Critics of *Writing Together* thought we spent too much on foreign participants. And it can be sterile to bring a writer thousands of miles to stay in a good hotel, 'meet' the public in a bookshop or hall, read a passage or two, answer questions, sign books and goes away. But when writers are genuinely mixing with each other and with a varied public (not just a gathering of academics) the results are always exciting. We've been careful to ask to

Writing Together people known to be communicators, arguers and mixers. Better a relatively little-known poet from the Sudan like Taban Lo Liyong, with an outgoing disposition, than world famous X who once (it is said) flew to a conference in Holland, objected to where he'd been placed in the programme, and flew straight home again; or cult superstar Y, at once swept off somewhere by groupies and never seen by anyone else.

When I taught in East Africa in 1968-71 Taban was by way of being famous - a prolific and controversial member of the generation of writers which emerged on the continent since 1950. Plenty of people have heard of him in the States and in Europe. Why when a London firm brought out several of his books at that time did he remain unknown to most readers in Britain?

The answer is 'ghettoisation'. Heinemann, whose African Writers Series took a dominant part in publishing the new African writers, were apparently more interested in selling big runs of books to African universities and schools where they would be set for study whenever nationalist thinking prevailed, than in marketing them in Britain. Ditto Longman, their major competitors. Since the books were already paperbacked, Penguin and other imprints widely available in Britain wouldn't lay hands on them. This was not so much the case with Caribbean writing, where Naipaul, Braithwaite, Walcott, Selvon, Lamming, found various different London publishers. Even so, there are important Caribbean titles you'd not see in Scottish bookshops because (presumably) we have few people of West Indian descent living here. *Black Marsden*, by Faber-published and world-famous Guyanese writer Wilson Harris, has not been discussed by Scottish critics, though set in Edinburgh. How many people have noticed that Kole Omotoso's first novel (in Heinemann African Writers' Series) *The Edifice* is also largely set in Edinburgh; or that Ghanaian Kodjo Laing, educated at Glasgow University, was acclaimed not long ago for a novel full of Scottish reference?

The position with Asian writing in English is even worse. Shirley Lim won the Commonwealth Poetry Prize for a book published by the oriental branch of a British multinational. The poetry of Nissim Ezekiel is published by OUP - but in India. Eunice de Souza's work was unobtainable in Britain, except in anthologies, without great effort until Polygon brought some out in Edinburgh this year (promptly rewarded with a Poetry Book Society Recommendation!). Kaiser Haq's translations into English from the rich stores of modern Bengali poetry are still, so far as I know, obtainable only in BanglaDesh, and perhaps in one or two specialist outlets in London.

Books by *white* South Africans are to the fore in Waterstone's, John Smith's, Thin's: but my attempts recently to buy novels by *blacks* writing about the townships were unsuccessful. (I could have ordered, but needed them in a hurry.) As for township poets, mostly published in Johannesburg by Ravan or Renoster, their well-produced books are invisible in Scotland. Only Mtshali, taken up by OUP, broke through the vision barrier years ago.

The position with 'White Commonwealth' is patchy. Fleur Adcock, long resident in London, acclaimed as a major feminist poet, is easy to come by. So are Patrick White, Margaret Atwood, Les Murray (latterly) and Alice Munro. But excellent work from Canada, Australia and New Zealand will be seen only by those tipped off to order from overseas. The same variegated supply is characteristic of US writing. Black US *women* are starred and superstarred. But interesting *regional* writers (I think of William Stafford the North-Western Poet, Walter Percy the New Orleanian novelist) have often been out of range of British readers. As for writing by major Americans (Indians), Tom Lowenstein's work on the culture of the Inuit of Alaska's North Shore shows us what wealth of experience we are missing.

As someone who once had the editorial task of proof-reading the annual bibliographical issues of the *Journal of Commonwealth Literature*, I can assure *Chapman* readers that there has been a spate of writing in English from the former Empire. Chris Wallace Crabbe, the Melbourne-based poet, was somewhat wry in his 1990 Trevor Reese Memorial Lecture at the Centre for Australian Studies in London, *Beyond the Cringe: Australian Cultural Overconfidence?*, about the current boom in Oz fiction. The Australia Council (itself "modelled in some ways on the Canada Council") has subsidised fiction so that where about 20 novels were published in 1973, 300 appeared in 1988. Wallace Crabbe is proud that whereas not so long ago "Australian books in a good bookshop would be presented on one small table, all the other books being filtered through English methods of cultural control", now "the bookshops, and even the better suburban newsagents, stock a wide array of Australian titles". But he quotes a respected scholar as remarking, "In no country ever, possibly, has it been easier to be published; we readers are flooded, and the mediocre tends to drive out the good."

I saw in Africa twenty years ago how the interest of British multinationals in producing books for a booming educational market, and of local firms in finding any authors at all, meant that work of little or no merit gushed into print. I have seen embarrassing remarks by well-meaning British critics who have suddenly woken up to the vitality of writing from Africa and have praised awful books, presumably because of some exotic appeal.

Meanwhile, interest in 'Commonwealth' writing, at a low ebb in Britain ten years ago, is growing again very healthily. The expansion of Women's Studies has stimulated interest not only in Atwood, Stead, Laurence and other fine 'White Commonwealth' writers, but also in novelists from the Indian sub-continent and the Caribbean. (The paucity of women's writing from most of Black Africa may occasion some rather grim socio-political thoughts.)

What is increasingly embarrassing is our neglect, in Scotland, of new European writing. I plead guilty myself: while I've paid attention to poets available in translation - once you read Holub, you don't forget him - I have read little continental fiction published since 1914, and almost none published since 1950. The committee of *Writing Together* wanted to give it a strong European dimension. We came up against intractable problems. First, the number of continental writers who might 'draw' a large audience here is tiny: Grass, Eco, Sagan, Duras, Havel, Kundera, Holub, Yevtushenko . . . Second, in one's ignorance, if we wanted a Catalan (we did) and Italians and Germans writing in dialect, how did we locate such people and fund them? In the event, come April, we got Dea Trier Mørch and Marianne Larsen, old friends, fluent in English, through the energetic Danish Institute; and Azouz Begag (so far untranslated) a charming man from Lyon whose fiction about his Algerian immigrant background has a growing audience in France. Italian,

The third and final phase of this International Festival of Writing in Glasgow from 12-23 September includes:

CHILDREN'S EVENTS - storytellings and workshops

WRITING FOR YOUTH? - a day conference on publishing and the place of writing in schools. Thursday 20 September

AN IRISH-ASIAN EVENING - a potent cultural mix of dance and poetry. Thursday 13 September

HOW TO GET PUBLISHED - a day for aspiring writers on 'Putting the Words Together' and 'Getting into Print'. Sat. 22 September

DAILY LUNCHTIME READINGS - at Glasgow's Glasgow and featuring writers such as James Berry (Caribbean), Nissim Ezekiel (India) and home-grown Aonghas MacNeacaill. 13-20 September

A MUTLICULTURAL MUSHAIRA - poetry from cultures as diverse as the Indian sub-continent, Africa, China, the Caribbean, Ireland and Scotland. Friday 21 September

WRITING TOGETHER writers will also feature in a MULTICULT-URAL BOOKFAIR, the WOMEN 2000 Conference, and participate in a CHAPMAN DAY to celebrate the 20th anniversary of the magazine on Sunday, 16 September in Glasgow's Glasgow.

Full programme for this feast of cultural delights available from:
Eleanor Commander (Administrator)
25 Elmbank Street, Glasgow G2 4PB
tel (041) 226 3431

Writing Together gratefully acknowledges the financial support of Strathclyde Regional Council, Glasgow District Council, the Scottish Arts Council, and the Arts Council of Great Britain.

Catalan and German participants, for different reasons, fell through.

I think poetry-readers generally are not too culpable. The Scottish Poetry Library has found good audiences over the years for poets from France, Finland, Italy, Denmark, and at this year's Edinburgh Festival Romanian women translated by Fleur Adcock. I think the grapevine alone would bring fifty people to hear a Greek or Norwegian poet new to Scotland.

But we are talking about a dedicated but small readership. Publishers such as Serpent's Tail, who produce, inter alia, Dea Trier Mørch's fiction in English, are taking horrid commercial risks in the vastly bigger market for novels. All the more reason to get the writers to Scotland. The first British publication of Ray Smith's refined fiction from Canada, by Polygon, followed his success here as Scottish Arts Council Canadian Writing Fellow.

So, I'm unrepentant about spending public funds (from Glasgow District and Strathclyde Region) on bringing writers from overseas to Glasgow in its Capital of Culture year. The young black British writer Marsha Prescod, in Scotland for the first time, read in a pub with some little-known Glasgow writers and said to me, 'Great! We must get these people to London.' That reading, like all the Writing Together events, had nothing to do with the High Culture for Big Sponsors and Tired Executives which some Glaswegian writers have fingered as the sinister concept dominating Glasgow 1990. I may as well make three personal points here. One is that I love classical music. (So does Tom Leonard.) Secondly, I am disgusted by prices for Pavarotti and other factors which imply that Culture is something expensive for the bourgeoisie. The third is that I wish the campaign against cultural elitism by the Glasgow left had been more selective in its attack on Glasgow 1990. It is sickening when writers one profoundly respects boycott Writing Together because it is funded from the same sources as other current ventures.

The aims of Writing Together go beyond 1990. I hope it will have stimulated other folk than our (very tired) committee to invite overseas writers to Scotland, take an interest in Afro-Caribbean and Asian writing, and see affinities between the Australian aborigine criminalised by oppression and the position of certain young people in Glasgow. After all, it's the radical nature of good writing which needs emphasising. To try to do it yourself is to get a new sense of yourself in the world. To read alertly the best others have written is to see why human society fails and must be changed; and why nevertheless life must be affirmed. To read foreign writers expands one's sense of life and of human possibility.

I had vowed, after some six or seven years of being continually involved in the hassle (mostly related to funds) of organising readings and other writers' events, to give it up completely. Let others pursue potential sponsors, cope with arguments about expenses, make tricky phonecalls to famous strangers . . . Then, this July, I went to a delightful symposium of Asian writers organised by David Dabydeen at the University of Warwick but refreshingly non-academic. Now, can any Chapman reader advise me where to get funds to bring to Scotland such fascinating companions as Saqi Farooqi, the major Urdu poet who lives in London, or Mahendra Solanki, based in Leicester? They should be heard here, maybe at a Scots-Asian event with a title yet to be devised. 'Scotch and Curry'?   Angus Calder

Ama Ata Aidoo

IN MEMORIAM THE GHANA DRAMA STUDIO

When you asked me
whether I felt at home coming back here,

I first shuddered,
remembering that actually,
The Ghana Drama Studio
was not pulled down: it was
uprooted.

By the time I got there
- just a few days before your question -
they had filled the monstrous hole the
operation left.

The ancients had said that
Home
is where your shrines flourish.
And the Ghana Drama Studio had been my shrine,
- of sorts.

I couldn't have called it a white elephant.

it was just an equally rare
gazelle
which slept under city neem,
away from the tropical morning glare,

                                            but

poised, always, for a cue
to spring into swift precise action.

But The Drama Studio is gone:
razed to the ground
to make way for someone's notion of
the kind of theatre
I
should
want.

When you asked me
whether I felt at home returning here,

I wondered how an old campaigner like you
could have asked a question
which the friendly and chatty taxi drivers who
bring me home here in Harare

                                  and elsewhere
would not ask.

And the forever pain around my heart
jumped, roaring for attention.

Because Comrade,
(holy places and their desecrations aside, and
not to mention the sacred duty
to feel at home on every little inch of
this mass of bartered and battered land which
I still, perhaps naively, call my own)

I had thought that folks like you'n'me had stopped
defining Home
from way way way back,   and have
calmly assumed that

Home
can be anyplace anywhere
where someone or other
is not trying to

roast your arse,
fry your mind, or
waste you and yours altogether . . .
Hm???

COMPARISONS II: WE WOMEN STILL!

Honestly, Sisters,
there is some elation here
. . . and bitterness too.

If you want to find out
how equal
          even
the more equal 1/2 of us are,
come see us at any
public library
- after a normal 9-5 working day.

We are there
in our numbers:
multi-racial
multi-national
multi-ethnic.

All middle-class of course.

Therefore,
fat.

But since fat is out
                    for the femmes fatales,
The Grease these days,
is often in the bones,
not on!

- and indulged. Like
favourite house-mice
scurrying through
the catalogues and
chumping up the bookshelves on
what was left

after the feast of the masters:

desperately hopeful too,
that
one day,
over-fed on crumbs but
armed with knowledge

we shall be permitted to
catch on:
lost momentum
lost hopes
lost plans
. . . life itself . . .

And our not-so-privileged sisters?

Honey,
they are
still at it; after even a
normal 9-5 working day,

taken up with
what's waiting of the
brutal loads that were
their lives and most painfully
abandoned,

before, long before 9 this morning.

A VERY ANGRY LETTER IN JANUARY

Dear Bank Manager,

I have received your letter.

Thank you very much:
threats,
intimidations, and all.

So what,
if you won't give me a loan?
Of two thousand, or
only conditioned by
special rules   and regulations?

Because I am   *not*
white
male   *or*
a "commercial farmer"?

(And in relation to the latter,
whose land is this anyway?)

I know that but for what I am not,
you could have signed

                     away
two solid millions, and
not many questions asked.

Of course I am angry.

Wouldn't you be if you were me?

Reading what you had written
was enough to spoil for me
all remaining eleven months of the year,
plus a half.

But I won't let it.

I had even thought
of asking God
that the next time round,
He makes me
white, male, and a "commercial" farmer.

But I won't.

Since apart from
the great poverty   and
the petty discriminations,

I have been happy
being me:

an African
a woman
and a writer

Just take your pragmatism
                your racism
                     your sexism
                         off me;

overt
covert   or
internalised.

And
damn you!   Ama Ata Aidoo

Nights by the Fire

Rebecca Scott

Rab stared into the drum fire and folded his arms to ward off the icy bite of the strong northerly wind. "Nae smokes, Tam?" he shouted across the flames.

"Smokes?" Tam asked. "I'm fed up giving you smokes."

Tam was a crusty, quick-tempered old bachelor of seventy. A life of bachelorhood was his own choosing, as he kept reminding his inebriated friends, saying it would be unfair to submit some nice wee lassie to a life of poverty with him.

"Anyway, you must have plenty smokes. I watched you collecting loads off the kerbs yesterday," Tam said.

"That's a bloody lie, I don't kerb crawl for nippers," Rab snapped at him.

"Well it wasn't fivers you were picking up, that's for sure." Tam shouted.

Rab went silent as Tam heaved a great sigh and shook his head. "I'll give you one then, but that's your last," Tam said as he slowly pulled an old black tin from his pocket. The tin was filled with old cigarette stubs. He began to break up the fragments of tobacco with his frail wrinkled fingers.

"Aye, you're not a bad old stick, Tam," Rab said as he slowly inhaled the smoke deep into his lungs and, with his eyes closed and head held back, he slowly blew the smoke upwards.

"My God, that's bloody good," he said.

Rab was twenty years younger than Tam. Unlike the old man, he had a wife and three children to his credit before embarking on his voyage to destruction. He thought himself a maverick: "Listen, lads," he would often say, "much as I've enjoyed these nights by the fire, I must move on." But Rab never did.

Tam looked tired as he seated himself on his black plastic bag beside the fire, his eyes searching the sky for the dreaded clouds, clouds that would determine whether Tam's tired bones had to assemble what bags he could carry to the tunnel three miles further on. He had grown quite fond of this open patch of grass, derelict wasteland that was once a site where rows of tightly packed houses stood, houses where neighbours shouted from windows to their children playing in the busy street. The only sound that Tam could hear now was the barking of stray dogs as they searched for scraps of food in the distance.

"Rab, is that big Joe?" Tam shouted as he strained his bloodshot eyes to see the approaching figure.

"You're late the night, big yin." Rab looked up at Joe with an inquiring look, which soon changed to relief, when his eyes fell on the bottle the tall man pulled from his pocket.

"Och I was blethering to this guy. He said he was a priest," Joe scoffed, as he passed the bottle to Rab and Tam.

"I didn't swallow it though, because he wasn't wearing a dog collar."

"Did he not try to convert you?" Rab asked, laughing.

"Convert me? Yes, he had a good try right enough. He said he would love to hear my confession - but do you know what I said to him?" Joe sat down on the bags and continued - "I said, well, you'll just need to bide your time and read it in the Sunday papers like everyone else."

Joe was a great husky fellow. The hard lines chiselled on his face helped to emphasise his large red nose. He, like Rab, had left behind a broken marriage and a few children here and there. He enjoyed boasting about his amorous conquests.

"Did you know that wee Tam here was a war hero, Joe?" Rab's speech was becoming slurred.

"A war hero? You're joking. Don't believe all he tells you."

Tam was staring into the embers of the fire with a limp expression on his face. Suddenly he sat up and pulled a small box from his pocket. "What's that then? Scotch mist?" he shouted angrily as he handed the box to Joe.

The big man opened the box with caution, his hands not quite steady.

"Well, I never . . . Look, Rab, it's a bloody medal."

Rab wiped the blood-red juice from his mouth with a quick brush of his sleeve. "That's a wee beauty, auld yin, What did you get that for?"

"I went to hell and back. That's what for."

"Yes, but whereabouts was this Hell?" Rab inquired.

"Have you ever heard of Dunkirk? . . . Well, that's where." Tam was becoming edgy, afraid that one of them might drop his treasured medal in the fire.

The two men watched the old man carefully place his precious decoration back in the box and slip it back in his pocket. He then curled up with his papers and plastic bags and soon fell into a deep sleep.

Rab and Joe drained the last drops of liquid from the bottle and pulled up closer to the fire, both knowing that if they moved beyond the circle of its warmth they would lose what little life they possessed.

"Did you know that Edgar Allen Poe was a drunkard?" Joe said in a whisper.

"God, yes, everybody knows that," Rab answered as he closed his eyes.

The grass was powdered with the first morning frost when Tam opened his eyes. He rubbed his hands vigorously and looked up at the dull leaden sky knowing it held no promise. He moved around staggering and stumbling in a vain attempt to gather up his papers and plastic bags, the 'survival kit' as Joe had labelled them.

Suddenly a look of thunder crossed his face as he pulled his pockets out and stooped to feel the lining of his coat.

"Right, c'mon, which one of you pigs nicked it?" he shouted.

"C'mon, the joke's over. Who's got it?" he repeated.

Joe slowly opened his eyes. "Got what?" he asked.

"My medal, that's what." Tam's body was shaking. His shaking this morning was not due to the usual reasons, the elements, or the beverage, but a burning rage inside him.

Joe stood up and put his outspread hands to his back, stretching as though afflicted with backache.

"Look, auld yin, sit down and calm yourself," Joe said, trying to quell the old man's anger.

Joe and Rab crawled around the ashes spilled by the brazier, in a vain attempt to find the cherished medal.

"I doubt you've dropped it on the fire, son," Rab said as he picked up a shiny object and quietly slipped it inside his coat.

"No I didn't, I had it in my pocket all night long," Tam answered wearily, the strain of his outburst leaving him exhausted.

Joe was oblivious to Tam's plea, his eyes were fixed on Rab. His face instantly flushed with rage. "Right, c'mon, Rab. Hand it over," he said.

A look of fear crossed Rab's face. "What? I've no got his bloody medal," he pleaded.

"Don't come it, I saw you picking something up and stashing it away in your pocket," Joe shouted as he pointed his finger in Rab's face.

"So I did, but it wasn't no medal," he protested.

"Well, it wouldn't be nippers either then," the old man cut in. "Picking up dog ends is beneath you, isn't it?"

Rab bent over and dug his hand deep into his left pocket and pulled out a silvery object. "There, that's what you saw me pick up," he said innocently.

Tam peered across to see what he held in his hand. "What is it?" he called to Joe.

"It's only a bit of tin," Joe replied.

"Are you keeping that to shave yourself, then?" Tam scoffed.

"No, it's a pullring off a can," he answered. "I'm saving them up,"

"Did you hear that, Tam? He's saving them up," Joe sneered.

"What do you get for saving up bits of tin, then?" Tam said with a sarcastic note.

"If I send away a hundred, I can get an anorak," Rab said, his voice shaking.

Joe's patience was wearing thin. Rab's secretive ways irritated him.

"Know something? I don't give a damn what you're saving for. I know I didn't pinch it, so that only leaves you," he shouted.

"Honest, I never pinched it," Rab pleaded.

Joe's face was rapidly turning red, as he stood rubbing his enormous knuckles with his left hand. Then he turned and lunged his fist forward.

Rab staggered back and slumped to the ground with a heavy thud. The two men stood quiet and listened as he lay on the ground groaning.

"You didn't need to hit him," Tam cried out loud.

"Och, I didn't mean to hit him so hard." Joe's voice was shaky as he gazed at the figure slumped beside the drum-fire.

Tam approached the fire very slowly, afraid to go too close to Rab. "Hey, Joe, he's stopped groaning. Do you think he's all right?"

"Right, get back out the way till I see," the tall man said as he cautiously approached the slumped heap. He nervously fumbled with the buttons on Rab's coat and, throwing the large lapels open, placed his ear against his chest. "Oh, God, there's no beat," he whispered in a trembling voice.

"There's blood on the back of his coat," Tam stuttered.

"He must have hit his head off that stone," Joe said, looking anxious.

"What will we do now?" Tam's voice was shaky.

"Well first off, you can give me a hand to pull him back from the fire," Joe replied. His thoughts started to race as he decided where to place the body.

"Quick, auld yin, you grab his feet and we'll drag him over to that tree," he shouted.

The old man puffed and panted heavily as he helped Joe place the body under the nearby tree. "I've cut my finger on something," Tam whimpered.

"Oh, God, have I not got enough to worry about?" Joe cried in despair.

"No ... I think it's a knife or something that was in Rab's coat," Tam cast an inquiring glance at Joe.

"Right then, open up his coat and we'll see," Joe said, becoming agitated.

The old man pulled the coat apart. There was no weapon hidden on Rab, only a noisy rattling sound coming from the lining of his coat. Tam pulled the lining open and released a shower of can pull-rings, which scattered like confetti round his feet.

There was a gasp from Tam and then nothing. There was a long silence, when both men stood with mouths wide open staring at each other. Their faces had a look of horror which quickly turned to remorse.

"It's all your bloody fault," Joe broke the silence. "You and your bloody medal."

Tam returned to the fire-drum and immediately began to collect his things. "I'm getting out of here quick, before the boys in blue appear."

"Yes, smartly ... I'm off as well," Joe replied as he turned to walk away. "Will you manage all right, auld yin?" he shouted, looking back.

"I'm fine ... I'll keep a low profile until it cools. Hey, you better do the same, big yin."

"Better make it the tunnel the night," Joe shouted back to him.

The old man rapidly tied up his bags and papers with an old piece of string, when he noticed something fall from the damp plastic bag he called his blanket. A look of terror crossed his face and he stood unable to move. This sorry medal was his award for killing; and now, he thought to himself, it was the basis for more killing. He stooped to pick it up. He held it so tightly clasped in his hand that his knuckles turned to a bloodless white. He began to walk slowly, dragging his steps. He walked on aimlessly as if in a trance, reproaching himself, realising that his accusations were unjust.

He heard the screeching of the seagulls, and caught the smell of stale fish. He realised he had reached the docks. Momentarily he thought of his friends awaiting the boats on the beaches all those many years ago. He thought of his friends who never saw the boats and remembered the colour of their blood on the sand. He thought of Rab's blood.

He unclasped his stiff fingers and stared down at the medal in his old, wrinkled hands. He spoke in a whisper. "No ... you're no worth it. After all you're only a bloody bit of tin." With a violent swipe of his arm he hurled it into the water.

Rebecca Scott

Marsha Prescod

BIG TIME

One day, my poem upped and said to me,
"Look kid, sorry to say this,
But whilst our relationship was meaningful,
It's time we chose our different paths."
"But I gave birth to you!" I wailed,
Whilst it threw a Dorothy Parker leer,
Swept out to see its analyst,
Leaving me to weep into my thesaurus.

From then on,
It was all downhill for me,
Only puns and epigrams
Shared my lonely life,
An affair with a passing sonnet
Came to nothing.

As years went by,
I glimpsed my former rhyme,
on the cover of Time, and Vogue,
Meeting with Popes and Presidents,
Profiled in the Sundays.

I saw my poem one last time
On the horizon,
Cruising in Gucci shades,
Talking out of the side of its mouth,
Doing deals with agent.
Tanned (from a skiing weekend with Jackie O)
It was smiling, deeply insincere,
Sitting, giving autographs to Mick,
And fixing up an interview on the Late Show.

And in sodden (but literate) misery
I yelled,
"You're nothing but a jumped up limerick!
I knew you when you were only a
Piece of graffitti . . ."
The last words I ever spoke,
For my poem sent
Heavies, in mohair Brooks Bros suits
To work me over
with copies of
Its Channel 4 contract.

Richard Fletcher

BURNING QUESTION

I had a lampshade once
that someone got from a Jew -
from his (or her) upper thigh,
in fact, and arse.
Skinning and curing
I do not understand
but it softened the glare
no worse than an Aryan's.
Someone put too big a bulb in
and the thing went up in smoke.
(History repeats itself,
First tragedy, then farce.)

A VICTORIAN SLOPPER DISCOURSES
ON THE OPERATION OF THE FREE MARKET

*'It is a time of great self-reliance. You live within your income. You have
great integrity and a great sense of duty. Yes, there are very difficult and
dark things, but the fact is that we are creating the extra wealth with which
to improve those conditions.'* (Margaret Thatcher, Prime Minister of Great
Britain, exhorting her subjects to a re-awakening of Victorian values in a
BBC TV interview, March 1982. Since quoted in the Open University Arts
Foundation Course TV broadcasts.)

I make moleskin trowsers, Ma'am. My day
is six in morn to ten at night. I get
eight pence a pair. Two pairs a day,
each week, twelve pair. In work I get
eight shillin just a week. From this
there's twist, thread, candles, coals. I clear
five shillin a week bare. Some weeks
there's little work. Last week,
but eighteen pence I cleart.
Takin all in all I make
three shillin clear a week. Three year
I been at sloppin, Ma'am.

Dad went when I were six. My Mam
is fifty turned. She washes pots.
After five doz her hands is cracked
and sore. The Public pays
four pence a doz. Ma'am - could you
keep yoursel on this? When first
I went to work, sixteen I were

and pure. The girls kept on at me -
'Trowsers pay slopper girls two ways,'
they'd say, and sin means clothes and food.
I knew t'were wrong, but how
to keep mysel and Mam on wage
the Masters paid? I couldn, so
I found mysel a tinman, twenty.
Twelve shillin, Ma'am, he made, each week!
He promised me he'd make me wife
and keep me and my Mam. Now babby's
comin and him six months not seen,
and all I see is streets.

What else is there for me, for any
slopper? Masters knows all this.
They know there's always streets.
They know we too must eat.
Ma'am - Masters in their broughams, they pass
us standing in the rain and call
us up and then next day dismiss
us for such wickedness. Would their
fine ladies understand? Would you,
Ma'am, understand? Would you? Ladies
revile our sin who've never wept
at moleskin or lain down with men
for bread. Wicked they call us,
wicked for needin bread.

I'd have lived on crusts and water
had I known. I'd grub and swallow
worms, same as moles whose skins I've sewn.
Each night I kneel with Mam, an' pray
the Lord will take our lives away,
for what use can they be to us
like this? What light is there? What light?
Why bring my babe to this, a slopper's
bastard, another mouth my mite
can't stretch to feed? A day, a night,
another and another night.
What shall I do, Ma'am?
Ma'am, what shall I do?

CAROL FROM AN ISLAND WITHOUT TREES

These are tunes of empty weather,
the sky too much a brawl
for wing and feather, rain
to corrode the vestiges of summer,
the Atlantic ransacking all,

storm-walls of sea-wrack flung
in the loveless clutch of bays.

Sing of a loveless island built
of this unloved weather,
shoreline of greys and ochre where
one seabird sprawls and slides
from citadel to citadel of gale.

Songs for the beak and claw
not wing and feather,
that gong in sea-caves,
rave of the ended summer
and nothing done,
the end of singing weather,
till the song, like wing and summer,
like feather and tune, is gone.

LETTER FROM DUBROVNIK

A year of silence, then news from Dubrovnik
on cheap, lined paper, scented with idleness
and warmer weather. You say, "I'm painting more."
Strange how your words imbue the images -
your finger smudging blue, sun on your nape,
a denim skirt, brown feet in espadrilles,
postcards, gouache, time-ground steps and all
those adriatic conversations adrift
in cul-de-sacs - the timelessness of art
and such fatuities.

                              Nothing is solved.
There's you, alone and older, striving for
the exact hue where sea and sunset meet
and I, pleased that you write, of course, and yet
alone and older too, and worse, adrift,
peering between your lines into regret.

FULL CIRCLE

It is as you said. The beacon
from the promontory beyond the wetlands
visits your little room and wakes
a shadow-dance along the mantle.
A cut flower artless in a jar. The clock.
A bowl of nectarines. A snap-shot - you and I
ringed in some distant calendar.

Illustration to 'Letter to Dubrovnik' by Kirsten Harris

And I and you, love, now in this veering light
have come to terms at last,
each by each forgiven and reprieved.

I cannot say how long the pact will keep,
for now trust only that our mood
has turned full circle - or perhaps
we see where lifetimes of wan hopes
have run aground. I will not ask.

I will dim the lamp and watch
your beauty wrap itself in sleep,
beyond the urge of flesh or gravity,
free from your questing fevers.

The forgotten yet familiar makes us weep -
that blemish in the cusp where neck meets shoulder,
eyelids I somehow never quite believed,
the fragment of my name, the way you stir
and turn and like the beam that sweeps the sea,
beckon and pardon me, and guide us home.

Richard Fletcher

James E McCormack

FROM WHERE SHE STOOD

The light in Sauchiehall Street precinct thins
Into its watery evening sheen,
Day's ease from golden to the white
That comes before the grey.

I am hindered by a flock
(I never saw before the picture of that word)
Of pigeons round a woman, feeding them
And, doubtless, quietly mad.

I stop and push my mind past metaphors
Of Christ and thousands fed
From scraped up loaves and fishes
Looking for what should be there for me.

She smiles, believing that I pause in admiration.
If she only knew.
She is herself the image, striking sharply home,
Her error just an etching, of the rest of us,
Assured we know the meaning to the world
Of what we do.

THE OTHER CITY

The castle keeps its place, gives point
To the sunshine. No move can be made,
Nothing seen, that is not framed by meaning
Drawn from time. Edinburgh waits, full of its
Own kind of assurance, free of the need
To explain, exempt from Glasgow's sense of
Requiring a ticket of admission to
Whatever's going on. Is there, though,
Beneath that comfortable, burgerlike
Balance, a calvinist unease, an
Itching in the spirit, Stevenson's sickbed
Sight of the life of different things? Neither
Good nor bad but only strange, and before
He bothers anyone else, Mister Hyde frightens
The virtuous life out of civil Doctor Jekyll.

FIGURE OF A WOMAN, FRAMED

Above the bed of earth around your window,
On withering bushes, the roses swarm and bob,
Pink insects, shifting gently in a slow wind.
Over the grey map of your sill the damp advances
On all fronts. From the street, I see that you
Are dark and pretty, perfectly got up,
A picture for an October afternoon.
Lust breathes less deeply, almost stirs awake.
(French films have given us our fantasies
Composed in shot.) What slows me is the silence
That is in the way you stand. I know
There is no sound behind you in the house.
Even the stereo has stopped. You smile because
My eyes have stayed too long upon their study.
I nod and walk on past. I know that you
Can see the roses and the damp and me
here on the road, but closer in you watch
Your eyes stare back at you from silent glass.

GREAT POET SEEN IN QUEEN STREET STATION

But only by me. On tiptoe across the concourse,
Face softer, fallen in a bit to easier corners,
Still the child's grave question from the smooth
Covers of his collections. Hungry and walking
Near the dangerous draw of the lavatories where
Men's starving eyes attack the crotches of others.

Howff of these anxious hunters, not so set
Apart as he is twice by craft and need from what
Is normally expected. Nervous step. At sixty still
A senior schoolboy, worried that his mum
Should learn his wants. His eyes were always
Wide behind his glasses. Step and look
As though his life has never found its ease
In this world nor a way to shut it out.

ON THE BEACH AT MUSSELBURGH, SATURDAY EVENING

No wind through Glasgow was ever white as this
Or crystal as this clear shining
That lets pass the moving dark.
Each at a distant end of the sand,
Two locals follow their demented dogs
As they conduct the nightly quarrel
With the sea's edge.
Up below the promenade,
The fourth and only other walker stops
For an innocent piss against the wall.

I am left, safe in the want of anything
Seeking attention, other than sea,
Sand and the white sky darkening.
A dozen working years at Zen
Might win this holy emptiness
That I have reached with only a well-judged drink
And the wonder Scotland wakes
Within my foreign soul.

TOPOGRAPHY

(In memory of Cathie Callaghan)

The stir of rocks has always left us fearful,
Opened hearts to what might be
If we have so misread this world
As to believe that things are constant
Under time's endorsement.
Water's skirl is there
To tell us certainty is found in flow.
The shapes of land lie out for us to see
The images we need
Of what the spirit thinks itself to be
Or strains to reach.

James E McCormack

The Asian Community in Scotland

The following is from an interview with Mohamed Bashir, head of Interpreting Services, a Glasgow-based project aimed at helping non-English-speaking communities at various points of need.

The history of people from the Indian sub-continent living in Scotland begins a long time back with the 'Lascars', a few Indian sailors who arrived in connection with trade. The substantial presence today dates more or less from the period of independence, when British India divided into the present state of India, and Pakistan, whose former eastern region is now BanglaDesh.

The many who knew British India and have not been back since 1948, would be surprised today by the extent of development of the country, or countries. India and Pakistan have industrialised, to some extent urbanised, where before 1948 most of the population were in agricultural work. Although agriculture was a major industry in British India, the Raj had made no attempts to mechanise; furthermore, hundreds of acres of land were unusable because of such problems as waterlogging and salinity. Soon after independence both India and Pakistan paid primary attention to development of agriculture, and the problems of waterlogging and salinity were overcome. Today even agricultural work is largely mechanised, where it had been a simple business of man and beast. There is of course poverty, but things have changed considerably. The Lascars were crewmen in what was for long a regular trade between India and Britain, transport of flax and cotton to be processed in British factories, and re-export of manufactured goods for resale in India. Now with facilities in the countries where the raw material grows, there is no need to transport it thousands of miles to be processed. Britain has lost that trade, and is suffering for having taken advantage of things as they once were. Indians have what they always had, and much cheaper. In many economic respects people who stayed in India or Pakistan have overtaken relatives who emigrated to Britain. But the population who were the first immigrants here were from very much undeveloped farming country. As long as there are corner shops they can work in them. But this no simple business.

Difficulties are considerable, and derive in part from the background of British India. For the majority of the population an education was not easy to obtain. It cost money, for everything, every book and pencil and hour of tuition. People did not learn to read, and did not learn English. Having come here unable to read or write, or speak English, many live in a strange situation unaware of, for instance, developments in computer technology. They do not know the modern world and what is possible in it. The former inhabitants of British India, labelled as today's Ethnic Minorities, were left illiterate due to no fault of their own, in many cases unable to communicate with their children born and bred in the United Kingdom.

One result is the terrible one that many schoolchildren get no career guidance. They come home with a form to fill in, to say what career they would like after leaving school. For the parents, an educated man's career is in something like medicine, or law. This being all they know of what an educated person's career could be, that is filled in on the form, without proper advice and consultation. The teacher or guidance teacher looks at the form, which says that the child and the parents have in mind one of these careers - and when as in most cases the child is unsuited to such a career, the teacher puts a line through "doctor" or the like, guesses where the child might go, and the child simply goes along that channel. It would be true to say that one result of this is that among the population in Britain, in Scotland, a lot of talent lacks the opportunity to make a contribution of enterprise to the economy. There is not the guidance necessary to realise the best.

There are of course many faults on different sides, many things go unrecognised, so things which should happen don't happen. The attempt is simply not being made to deal with the particular difficulties which exist today. A lot of words are spoken, but at government level there does not seem to be an understanding of the very complicated situation. There is also a problem in that community leaders do not always do the work of disseminating information where it is needed, among the population. Some people who get themselves into prominent positions are often what can be called glory-seekers. They turn up at meetings where things are discussed, where there is information, but regard their access to this as no more than a mark of their status. They are flattered, but do not do the work of letting people know what they should, the information is not properly disseminated. Whatever government may say about all that is being done, the position is much more complicated; community leaders are not in every case doing what it is assumed they are doing.

There is a problem of attitude. Many people have come to Scotland from India and Pakistan, and there has been very little trouble, unlike in parts of the South. This is because in Scotland there has been a long continuity of different peoples coming in and being accepted. Yet especially in official agencies the attitude which prevails is not so simple.

Take one case involving a British government employee in Scotland, a man from Pakistan. His daughters were to be married, and close family were invited, some twenty of them from Pakistan. He filled in the forms and as their sponsor signed the declaration that these were legitimate visitors, his uncles and other relatives. They had to pay a fee of one thousand rupees in application for a visa, and travel to Islamabad, for some a long way, to have their applications considered. What happened was that, of the twenty, British immigration denied *twelve* applications! A telephone call was made to Islamabad from Glasgow to explain. These were some of them great-uncles of the girls getting married, prosperous businessmen who in several cases owned factories; certainly not penniless individuals whose return to Pakistan was in doubt. They were better off there than their relatives in Britain.

All this was painstakingly related. In the event only one more application was allowed, a total of nine out of twenty. Now the man who testified to immigration authorities as regards the legitimacy of these applications was a British Civil Servant: one of their own people. What can be made of a situation where Britain does not trust one of its own Civil Servants? What was the basis of the decision to allow only nine visitors out of the twenty?

Take equally the case in America, Australia or anywhere immigrants from Britain have made new lives for themselves and had some success. Like them Asians in Britain would like to spend time with their parents, but with families and responsibilities it would be inconvenient and practically speaking difficult for them to go back to visit. Yet these respectable businesspeople in the British economy are not allowed a visit from two elderly grandparents; because they cannot get visas. There is some evidence of racism, but certainly a real inconsistency in the way some people are being regarded.

Take also what happens with inspectors employed to enforce hygiene regulations in restaurants. Not so long ago there was a lot of specific attention to Asian establishments. In one case a proprietor spent a lot of money on extensive work to meet the inspector's demands. Eventually the man was got to agree that things were more than satisfactory, and that was that. But that inspector was transferred soon after, a new inspector came, and began to tell the same proprietor that this and that needed to be done. An independent Asian arbitrator had secured the previous inspector's agreement, and to him this new inspector spoke of what was necessary with "these people". The arbitrator believes that he gave the inspector a lecture he could remember to tell his grandchildren. What did he know of a Moslem household, and the cleanliness insisted on? Moslems do not sit in baths of water with the dirt from their bottoms in it splashing it all over their bodies. What did the inspector know of "these people"? There is considerable lack of understanding of the people. The problems which exist are not understood either, and there is also waste from attention to false problems.

The problem of glory-seekers has to be understood in another respect. If they do not bring the people into touch with important facts of the modern world around them, this is particularly bad because of the nature of the population they are wrongly assumed to be serving. The official assumption is that things which cannot do so are being expected to look after themselves. There are broadly speaking bad people, the same as anywhere else. But there is only so much that the good people, the real representatives can and should be expected to be able to do. There is no single cohesive community, not only because of differences between Indians and Pakistanis, but because Pakistanis differ among themselves, as Indians do too. Official provisions fall short, particularly because there is no recognition of the differences internal to the ethnic population. The necessary unity does not exist. Without it difficulties will not decrease. There is need for effort within the minority ethnic community, *and* in organisation of bodies and agencies intended to serve it.

The communities themselves have further problems of culture where younger people are interested only in such activities as, say, discos. Their religion and culture are being left behind, and who is to look after the identity of people in that situation? They need a unity they do not have, and there are factors liable to increase the problem of existing disunity. It is essential a successful effort be made to understand the position and the people in it, deal with questions of communication, reduction of disorganisation, various social provisions, guidance, not least education.

Mohamed Bashir

THE ROSEMARY ARTHUR AWARD

There are many poets whose work warrants publication in book form. This award provides for :

The funding for a perfectly bound book
£100 in cash
A suitably inscribed clock

To be eligible a poet must not previously have had a book published and must be a resident of the U.K.

At any time during the year but before December 31st, a poet may submit between 20 and 40 poems together with a £5 reading fee and a suitable s.a.e. for the work's return to:

The National Poetry Foundation
27 Mill Road
Fareham
Hants PO16 0TH
Tel: 0329 822218

The winner will be announced on February 3rd each year.

NB. The name of the entrant must not appear on the poems but, together with any acknowledgements, must appear on a seperate sheet.

*****

Rosemary Arthur has Covenanted a suitable sum each year until her death for this award and has altered her Will so that the NPF will a receive a 'substantial sum' in Trust upon her death to assure the award into the foreseeable future.

No Trustee of NPF past or present, or friend or relationship of such a Trustee, shall be eligible for consideration for this award; nor will being a subscriber to the NPF elicit especial consideration in any entry for the award.

Martin Marroni

A PARABLE OF THE WORD

A man crouches on church steps
bellowing mutely to a cobbled square.
Pigeons wander uncrossing paths
as he rants in silence, brandishing
a crucifix, image of his calvary
inset between stone Virgin and St. John.

Pedestrians pass on the other side
or look away, surmise him mad
in all directions preaching shirtless
to the Sunday streets. He stands, extends
his arms, transfixion of the evening sun,
to those with ears to hear him.

No one breathes "Amen". The silence
leans intent, appealing, from the confines
of this pulpit wall. He speaks in parables,
caricature of every dumb frustration
seeking words as yet unsaid, of love
and fear, what is and what is not:

heart full of meaning, mouth of air,
mortality beneath the stones of God,
the cliche of existence. He goes, his jacket on,
his shoulder bag in rhythm with his stride,
mad merely whence the spirit blows. Pigeons
scavenge up the steps on which he stood.

THIEVES IN THE MARMOTTAN

On 27 October 1985 in a daylight raid, thieves stole nine paintings worth over
£10m from the Marmottan Museum in Paris. Among these was Monet's
'Impression, Sunrise', which gave its name to the Impressionist movement.

Tearing canvas from the frame
what was their expertise?
Reports precisely name
the paintings: Monet's 'Sunrise'

taken in a daylight raid
and other eight - impressions
worth ten million pounds it's said.
Connoisseurs of evocations

from the past, they stole
a movement's monicker - and more,
disturbed a peace as cool
as waterlily ponds. A score

of other experts dust the place
and if they could would prise
the echoes from the walls, trace
scents now indistinct and analyse

each instant's canvas as though life
were paint. The room we shared
was televised, fish-lensed. Grief
came first, then rage - they dared!

and then I laughed - thieves had left
our image, and investigations of the crime
had overlooked our priceless theft
of moments from the frame of time.

SAND DANCE

Small as my eye, the sandcrab watches me.
I lie, quiet as a beach. His feelers sift
my rhythm from the brushstrokes of the sea
behind. Unsure of me, his legs contract to lift

the carapace. Smaller than the sandgrains
constellating round, the eyepoints glitter on their stalks.
The sun burns my back; a noisome insect strains
my stillness. Movement comes. The crab unlocks

and flows into his burrow. These nervous forays
out and back assume the patterns of a dance.
I play a hornpipe in my mind and with each phrase
the crablegs, soft-shoe-shuffling, retreat, advance.

Ash grey like sand he is, the only tint
false eyes below the stalks, his life unrolls
in syncopation with the sea, his movement
always sideways to my square-set goals.

I think my watching, unlike his, stands me apart,
my eyes observe the motion, but my thoughts
reduce it to design - the living process of the heart
to end and purpose, blind hypnotic spots.

And yet, aware or not, it is my turn
to step, to sense myself progressing side to side,
and in the weaving of the rhythm learn
how finite measures ebb and flow like tide.

Again the crab prepares to move, legs jacked
above the burrow, reflex set - the arc
a figure of the integrated self, all poles intact,
convex to light, and cupped to hold the dark.

MASS IN ST. MARK'S CATHEDRAL, VENICE

The floor slopes leftward in the church of Mark
across the nave's grain.
Columns and domes designed for elevation
squat to still the undulating mud beneath.

Seeping from walls the celebrant's voice
is a mosaic of amplified syllables, and meaning
ricochets and fades among scraping chairs
and those for whom the sacrifice is inconvenience.

The demotic mass, its service shorn of choir and pomp
its altar now demountable and there to touch,
a gilded lion on its back, has little power to move
when history dominates eternity.

Words are difficult to extricate from stone,
bare gospel of a man, not dogma yet nor moral scheme,
like relics filched from an Alexandrian tomb
were bones enough to build an empire on.

Now people sit in rightward tilts to stay upright.

Below the marble arabesques
a million piles of ancient wood
quiver slowly in the silt, and when I stand
my right knee bends in reflex genuflection.

MELTEMI

When will it stop, this rasping wind,
hacking like a summer cough, breathing
ghosts from dry clay? or burst
to life, this matchhead, sparking not igniting
in its futile strikes against the earth,
sulphuring the air with acrid perfumes
from the scrub? Last night at dinner
it lurched around, a drunkard, couping
wine and snatching words from mouths   -

Then it was my friend: I too had drunk
and guessed those words and made them soft,
seduced myself with vacuous syllables,
gave substance to some ancient god of Crete,
or love, conjured from the beached youths
that people this summer coast and share
the Babel tongue, the Kerouac imperative,
while the wind snatched doilies to the roof
and scattered, too, the bones of a picked fish.

You sleep now, fitful, puffing sharply
through your nose to clear from it the layers of dust
that, given time, would bury you. Perhaps
you think you are the wind, tugging
at clothes, tangling limbs like branches,
flipping pebbles with your tongue - and yes,
your passion, hot and dry, going only
where the next gust takes you. But then,
perhaps you thought the wind was me.

It is dawn now. The sky is open
while the canopy of cicadas awaits the sun.
On such another dawn I'll pack and go
beyond the mountains and the heartland of this storm
to where my life still waits for me.
I look across the bay. Gust-whipped ripples
make patterns of a darker hue. What wind
is this whose blast can bend a tree
yet, save for shadows, leaves undisturbed the sea?

Martin Marroni

Mike Jenkins

LETTER TO INDREK, (Estonian poet)

I'm here on the mountain,
often forgetting how high
from the sea: even the wind
Hasn't the power to remind me,
though rushes wave.

I make an extension
on our oak. It pays
not in brick-bound stock:
a mouse-like bird
comes to startle.

It doesn't *creep*
but scampers along bark
seeking grubs as it goes.
If only my country
were like that,
defying what we call it.

The names we give ourselves
are constantly battling,
cannot hope to balance
between air and tree
the way that bird . . .

You tell me of your home:
how those books are bought
like prints of the imagination
to be shared, not stored away
in attics and cellars
with immortality as the lesson.

In these days after Christmas
high street videos bring them in
with action, action, action:
so much happening
they cannot move.

Enough of this, our words are "flighting".
Snow may come from the east.
For the first time, an owl
hollows out the night
into a wind instrument.
In Estonia, in Cymru
we will listen.

IMPLANTING OF STONE

We visit our dead
through the opening
to watch them ripen and burst,
dispersing on their journeys,
with a mast of their bones,
taking earth-won possessions.

Chieftain in his bed of axe-heads,
shell-jewellery and grain,
while our tribesfolk in small tombs
have just a pot or necklace to bring.

Engravings we made on the sky
of ceiling, so their other-beings could see
familiar shapes in the stars.
the mother-goddess with her breasts
ready to feed them wherever they go.

Line circling line: we've etched
the currents of the other-world,
tangible as grooves on our hands,
ploughlines and striations on a shell.

2.

The hauling of huge slabs,
rolling them over logs.

The sweat falling like insects
into our eyes, stinging them.

The moans like the pains
of labour: pushing, always pushing.

Hands cut by wolves' teeth,
feet by claws of the bear.

Our wooden huts distant in dust.
Our fields and animals like pools and fish.

We hold the slabs in balance.
This is the final entrance,

where one day we'll set off sailing
on a sea without a coast.

3.

When the rain doesn't fall
all we have is blood:

the gods must eat
like the rest of us.

We've implanted these menhirs
as paths for the sun to tread

so he may raise his offspring:
fruits of green and red;

as a lying-down for the moon
so she, in her fullness, is the light

we spin with our night-calling.
Then in the total eclipse

we share the union of sun and moon,
as darkness comes with man and woman.

TINKER'S WAR

I.

No longer the coastline
with its cliff-long greeting,
or Shropshire's hull-shaped edge
tugging me home:
each horizon a step
beyond the mist of tiredness
our duties always bring.

Routine thrown like bilge.
The ensign flapping
our fears, our expectations.

At school, I drew obsessively
Union flags: distant windows,
disparate thoughts. Now, at last,
they move as one:
our Task Force parting the waters.

Dressed in my father's army cap,
holster and water-bottle weighed me down:
strutting his map of the Western Front,
a porthole into his past.
My reflection grew
like a fairground mirror
in the Russian cooking-pot
I'd polished from grime to gold.

Sent off with drums and yells.
The dock-hands work like coolies.
Officers and men forget petty regulations
and humour from the sailors
propels us at greater knots.
The captain's court-martial
is left behind with Portsmouth
and the Old World.

Ascencion, St. Helena . . . our colonies
will signpost the way.
Sixteen warships - the paperwork
and punishments like dots of islands -
with a purpose where there was none,
with 'V' from each one's wake.

2.

This may be the last thing
before the missiles come.
What will you think of me,
you fish who fin past
a strange, thin creature
with smudged markings?
Will you accidentally gulp
this piece of England?

I have to speak out
because I was living an illusion,
like those Blighty music-hall songs.

The victims will be consigned
with this: to be lost
like tiny moulds of history
pressed in the strata.

Nothing I do has meaning anymore
except this communion, away
from orders I take and give
like possessions stolen from my parents,
books bound with caring.

Our ships trench the waves.
Rapidly towards those rocks
it isn't my mortality I protect,
but my sanity: to see still
how we're wrangling over some stamp
we'd kept in the attic too long.

Malvinas.
Falklands.
Surely somebody can interpret?

But who am I talking to?
This paper will disintegrate
and words rise up as insubstantial bubbles:
the breath before we drown.

David Tinker died in the Falklands War when the HMS Glamorgan was hit by an exocet. Later A Message from the Falklands *was published, which contained his letters.*

IN THE PRECINCT

Rows of shops CUT PRICE KWIK SAVE.
People on look-out for bargains,
dart-eyed. Teenagers lean over
walkways, smoke and spit
and focus quick on parts of women:
piling remarks like frozen chops . . .
curse and cut . . . no blood . . . not yet!

Backed by video and CD recorders
two youths chest out newspapers, spied on by mannequins
in the latest stripes. One
ragged, long black hair straggled;
the other with convict style and mercenary boots,
tattoo of Union Jack out-muscling red dragon
and NF a brand in black.

The bored boys above see them
stark against the lip-shine of windows:
staying put, like them, while everyone else
has a place to go.

Mike Jenkins

The Urchin of the Chaâba
from Le Gone du Chaâba
Azouz Begag

Zidouma's doing a washing this morning. She's got up early to take over the only source of water in the shanty-town: a hand-pump which draws drinkable Rhone water. In the small brick basin Berthier invented to water his garden, she's rubbing, slapping on the concrete and wringing cloths heavy with water.

Bent at right angles, she soaps, then works the pump once, twice, to draw water. She rubs again, rinses, draws water, wrings out the linen with her muscular pair of arms, never finished repeating these operations. Time is passing. She knows very well the Chaâba has only the one well, but from her manner it's plain she's going to please herself, bent on taking her time, a lot of time. If somebody drops the least remark, he'll not have troubles to seek.

Right enough, that somebody's waiting a few yards away: the neighbour from the huts stuck up close to Zidouma's own. Two-handed she's holding a bucket that shows evidence of dirty linen, children's clothing, clouts and dusters. Patient. Patient. Zidouma, tireless, doesn't deign to look in her direction, even if already for some minutes aware of a presence behind her showing signs of irritation. And she's in fact moving more slowly.

And the neighbour always patient, alw . . . No: she's patient no more. Letting her bucket drop, she's charging like a billy-goat at her rival. The impact is dreadful. The two women are grabbing hold of each other through a lot of deep-throated battle-cries.

Drawn by the excitement, other women are coming from the rows of huts. One of them, from one of the two clans that make up the community, is putting herself between the two warring parties to try to appease their feelings. Supposedly to calm the more excited one, she delivers a dreadful back-hander to her right cheek. It takes no more for my mother to throw herself into the melee. Leaving me to my café au lait she's setting her solid frame in motion, cursing away.

I don't try: you don't hold back a moving rhinoceros. I finish my drink in a rush to help the fighter. I know not why, I like to sit on the house steps enjoying the scenes played at the pump. It's so strange to see women thump each other.

Clan against clan, behind the tenors of the Chaâba, my mother and my Aunt Zidouma, the women are poisoning life for themselves.

- May Allah put out your eyes, one of them's wishing.

- I hope the place goes on fire tonight, bitch, and you die in your sleep, the other retorts.

I didn't know women had such resources. Even my mother - she doesn't come last in this among them. Whenever there's an outbreak of war, they rip their dresses and their skin, pull out hair, throw sheets and clothes, all newly washed, into the garden dirt, scarting the backs of their throats to give out the most extreme and coloured expressions of scorn; they throw the very worst at each other. I'm very fond of this theatre. One day I even saw Zidouma making a funny sign with her hand and saying to another woman from my mother's clan:

- Well, you can have that.

She held up her right hand, all the fingers bent bar the middle one, and that straight up. The other woman came out with abuse like a demon, totally hysterical. She lifted up her dress with her left hand, slowly bending her back, then sticking out a white backside, on a giant scale. Her naked sex, covered up completely by her hand, served as her argument in the war of nerves. I found this ceremony odd. However the actress, catching sight of my exploring look, concealed her play. I blushed without knowing why.

The pump is only an excuse. In reality none of the women does any work, from dawn to dusk, dusk to dawn, sealed within the corrugated iron on the boards of the shanty-town. The roster for cleaning the yard, the garden, the lavatory, is little respected. The nerves fail easily.

After any altercation, the women hope to be able to hate each other till their lives' end, but, inexorably, the following morning's light of day extinguishes the braziers of the vigil. Nothing changes with regard to this place: the hutments are always in the same place, planted, and nobody disarranges a thing. The one watersource is forever the only one in the oasis.

In the Chaâba, hatreds are not possible for more than a matter of hours. Besides, following the riots in front of the pump, the women always lay out jerrycans of water in their huts. They do their washing in a basin,

In the evening, when the men get back from work, no echo reaches them of what's happened while they were absent from the Chaâba. The women hold their tongues, saying to themselves that with all the hard conditions of life they have nothing to gain from sowing enmity among the men.

* * *

I had to sit at a desk with Jean-Marc Laville. I'd have liked to show Moussaoui and the other cousins that that's not what I wanted, but that was impossible: the suggestion came from the teacher, and if I wanted one day to be top of the class it was necessary I followed it.

They all looked at me with scorn as they went back to the bottom of the class, as if waiting for me to dare the teacher's authority that morning. Jean-Marc tried to speak to me. I believe he asked me if I wanted to sit on the right or the left of the desk, and I said to be quiet since M. Grand was speaking. I didn't want the cousins to see me swapping words with him.

Everybody's sitting down now. The teacher stands up at his desk and starts speaking.

- Today the morals class, hygiene, he says.

And for some minutes he went on about cleanliness, asked questions like: must one be clean and tidy? How many times a day need one wash? The French pupils replied with alacrity to everything they knew well from home. They spoke of baths, washing, cleaning your teeth, toothpaste. At the Chaâba, if it was realised that the rules of cleanliness demand such minute attention to detail, there would be a lot of laughing. To wash the mouth, any adult there would take a tumblerful of water into his mouth, draw in his cheeks to send it round his teeth, take a finger over the incisors to clean the surface, make new waves in the mouth and finally with a great spit empty out the dirty water. You can hear them after that hawking the back of their throats to get out the impurities of the day before, and propelling them to the tarmac. Then with a foot they cover that stuff up to avoid revolting their neighbours. There it is. No need of brushing teeth or of Colgate.

- What is needed to do a good job of washing yourself? the teacher asks.
Three pupils raise fingers.
- Sir! Sir! they chirrup like new-hatched chicks in a nest.
M. Grand waits a moment as others ask, then reformulates the question.
- With what do you wash every morning?
- Sir! Sir! the daring ones are all the time cheeping.
- Jean-Marc, goes the teacher, pointing a finger toward him.
Up he stands:
- A flannel and some soap.
- Good. And what else?
- Some shampoo! says somebody else.
- Yes. And what else again?
I have a brainwave. Instinctively I lift a finger to the sky, paying no notice to reproachful looks the cousins have for some time been giving me.
- Azouz! M. Grand permits me to speak.
- Sir, you need too a *chritte* and a *kaissa*!
- You need *what*? he goes, eyes wide with stupefaction.
- A *chritte* and a *kaissa*! I say three times louder than before, under the impression something not normal is happening.
- What *is* that? the teacher asks again, amused.
- Something you put on your hand to wash yourself with.
- A toilet glove?
- I don't know, sir.
- What's it made up of?
I explain to him.
- That's what it is, a toilet glove. At home you call it a *kaissa*?
- Yes, sir. But I only use it when I go to the baths with my mother.
- And a *chritte*, then: what's that?
- Well, sir, it's like a lot of bits of string twisted together, and sort of scrapes you, quite a lot. My mother rubs me with it, and I get all red.
- That's what you call a horsehair mitt, he ends smiling.
I redden a bit but he encourages me:
- It's good to have let us learn that, whatever!
After a short silence he begins again on the theory of hygiene. I work out that at the Chaaba we're very bad practitioners, but don't say so.
- Now, he starts again, after having spoken for half an hour, you will all take off your socks and lay them flat on the tops of your desks. I want to see that every one of you is clean.
A horrible dread takes me by the throat. It fades quickly as I remember my mother made me put on clean socks that morning. All round me there's

utter silence, then all the pupils bend down to undo their shoelaces. I do this myself, put my nose into my socks to try the perfume. Hum! Fair enough. I'm won't be too badly ridiculed. Beside me, Jean-Marc stretches out on the desk-top the immaculate colours of his nylon socks. M. Grand walks between the rows, nabs here and there several samples, doing well to avoid sniffing too deeply, but turning them over in every sense to study spots, stains, holes.

- Not very clean, that! Very good! says he to this one and that.

While some are proud of coming up to the appropriate standard, others curse themselves for not having thought to change their socks this morning.

M. Grand comes toward Moussaoui and his gang. No socks on the desk.

- Mossaoui, take off your socks and put them at once on the desk, he says calmly.

The pupil hesitates for several moments, sends his gaze toward the window and, at long last, resolves to speak, fixing on the teacher.

- My socks. Me, I'm not going to take them off. Why should I, anyway? This isn't the public health service? Worse, too, you're not my father, to give me orders. I'm not taking my socks off. It's not worth waiting.

M. Grand goes red at once, shocked rigid. This has to be the first time in his career that he's been made face such a rebellion.

Mossaoui holds out, never more determined. Maybe he has, after all, some regard for his adversary's nostrils?

- You have dirty feet. That's why you don't want to take off your socks, is the teacher's rejoinder: but the words are *Tu as les pieds sales ... tu ne veux pas*. Unthinkingly he's using the familiar form of address to his pupil.

The unbelievable happens. Moussaoui strikes down the sickly smile with a look of scorn, before throwing at him:

- You're nothing but a poof! Sod off, you!

A frosty chill mortifies the class. A few moments, and you can hear the teacher stammer. His words aren't getting past his lips. He's lost face. Moussaoui's getting bold, standing up. His back to the window, sideways on to the teacher, fists screwed up, he's shouting:

- If you want a fight, poof, come on. *I'm* not afraid of you!

M. Grand can hardly smile at this. He goes back to his desk and, not looking at Moussaoui, says to him:

- This will be dealt with in the headmaster's room.

The cousin sits back down relaxing his pose.

- The headmaster? I snap my fingers at him. And at you.

- You'll be expelled from the school, miserable idiot.

Moussaoui has another jibe, playing on *tu* and *vous*.

- That will do for now, the teacher's saying, before I lose my temper for good and all.

- Lose it! Lose your temper! the rebel's getting worked up again, jinking from leg to leg like Muhammad Ali. Come on! Come on! I'm waiting!

- It looks like this lunatic will have to be locked up, M. Grand says, turning towards us.

- Poof! Moussaoui repeats, spitting out the P.

- Carry on! You'll be pleased enough when your folks stop getting the family allowance!

These last words pole-axe Moussaoui. The argument bites. Get expelled from school: so what? but when it touches your father's pocket that you won't show the teacher your socks, no! Fear shows in his face, his eyes drop towards his desk, defeated. Half-dead he mutters again a few incomprehensible words, then a sudden light flashes through his whole body.

- You're all of you racists! he howls. It's because we're Arabs that you can't stand, us!

- M. Grand has his cards in his hands. He goes on the offensive:

- Don't try to defend yourself that way. The truth is, you're an idler, and idlers like you never do anything in life.

- What a poof! goes Moussaoui, turning toward Nasser. He thinks we don't understand why we're always put bottom of the class.

Fearful as he is, Nasser doesn't know where to hide his face. He doesn't like the idea of having his folk's family allowance cut off.

- Liar! M. Grand follows up. Look at Azouz - all heads turn toward me - he's an Arab too, but for all that second top of the class. Stop looking for an excuse. You're just a lazy dolt.

The response nails me to my seat. Why me? What idea did the teacher have, sending me to the front. Moussaoui's mouth is open above his jotter. On the verge of another rejoinder, to demonstrate to the teacher that he is a racist, and here is fact implacably staring him in the face. And the king's personal sheikh. On account of me!

With these final words from the teacher echoing in the classroom and in my head, the normal routine resumes. M. Grand is again speaking normally, but as he speaks Moussaoui and his confederates, down below in the donkeys' corner, are talking loudly in Arabic, grinning, moving about in their seats. Although this is assuming the character of a rebellion, the teacher remains as marble. As for me, I no more exist, no more listen, afraid of the cousins' reprisals.

Minutes later, the bell stirs me from torpor. As we move to the playground, several French pupils are making comments in a low voice about the coup d'état by the Arabs at the foot of the class. Yet once more I repel Jean-Marc Laville's attempt to maintain a relationship between us as members of an elite.

- He's forever annoying us, and then he calls us racists! I don't like that guy. What about you? he confided.

- It's not my problem! I replied to him brutally.

And he went over to join his own sort again.

Azouz Begag
Translated from the French by Robert Calder

Liz Lochhead

BAGPIPE MUSIC, GLASGOW 1989

When A. and R. men hit the street
To sign up every second band they meet
Then marketing men will spill out spiel
About how us Glesca folk are really *real*
(Where once they used to fear and pity
These days they glamourise and patronise our city -
Accentwise once they could hear bugger all
That was not low, glottal or gutteral.
Now we've "Kudos" incident'ly
And the Patter's street-smart, strictly state-of-the-art
And our oaths are user-friendly)

It's all go the sandblaster, it's all go Tutti Frutti
All we want is a wally close with Rennie MacKintosh putti.

Malkie Machismo invented a gismo for making whisky oot o girders
He tasted it, came back for mair, and soon he was on to his thirders
Rabbie Burns turned in his grave and dunted Hugh MacDiarmid
Said: It's oor National Thorn, John Barleycorn but I doot we'll ever learn it.

It's all go the Rotary Club, it's all go "The Toast Tae The Lassies"
It's all go Holy Willie's Prayer and plunging your dirk in the haggis.

Robbie Coltrane flew Caledonian MacBrayne
To Lewis . . . on a Sunday!
Protesting Wee Frees fed him anti-freeze
(why God knows) till he was comatose
And didnae wake up till the Monday.

Ay it's Retro Time for Northern Soul and the whoop and the skirl o the saxes.
All they'll score's more groundglass heroin and venison filofaxes
The rent boys preen on Buchanan Street, their boas are made of vulture
It's all go the January sales in the Future City of Culture

It's all go the P.R. campaign and a radical change of image -
Write Saatchi and Saatchi a blank cheque to pay them for the damage.

Tam o' Shanter fell asleep
To the sound of fairy laughter
Woke up on the cold-heather hillside
To find it was ten years after
And it's all go (again) the Devolution Debate and
                pro . . . pro . . . proportional representation
Over pasta and pesto in a Byres Road Bistro,
                Scotland declares hersel' a nation

Margo McDonald spruced up her spouse for the Govan by-election
The voters they selectit him in a sideyways *left* defection
The labour man was awfy hurt, he'd dependit on the X-fillers
And the so-and-sos had betrayed him for thirty pieces of Sillars!

Once it was no go the S.N.P., they were jeered at as "Tory" and "tartan"
And thought to be very little to do with the price of spam in Dumbarton
Now it's all go The Nationalists, the toast of the folk and the famous
- of Billy Connolly, Muriel Gray, and the Auchtermuchty Proclaimers

It's all go L.A. lager, it's all go the campaign for an Assembly
It's all go Saor Alba and winning ten-nil at Wembley.

Are there separatist dreams in the glens and the schemes?
Well . . . it doesny take Taggart to detect it!
Or to jalouse why we hate the Government
Is that we patently didnae elect it.
So - watch out, Margaret Thatcher, and tak tent Neil Kinnock
Or we'll tak the United Kingdom and brekk it like a bannock.

AFTER THE WAR

for Susanne Ehrhardt

After the war was the dull country I was born in.

The night of Stafford Cripps's budget
my dad inhaled the blue haze of one last Capstan
then packed it in. "You were just months old." The Berlin airlift . . .
A.T.S. and REME badges rattled in our buttonbox.

Were they surprised how everything was different now?
Did it cheese them off that it was just the same?
Stuck in one room upstairs at my grandma's
rammed against the bars of my cot and one
mended featherstitch jumper on the winterdykes,
the puffed and married maroon counterpane
reflected in the swinging mirror of the wardrobe,
radio plays, them loving one another biting pillows
in the dark while I was sleeping?
All the unmarried uncles were restless
champing at the bit for New Zealand, The Black Country, Corby.
My aunties saved up for the New Look.

By International Refugee Year
We had a square green lawn and a twelve inch tele

                                        Liz Lochhead

Michael Henry

ROSLIN CASTLE

Walking down a disused railway track
I arrive at a station platform
with red sandstone slabs sloping down
like ramps. An old crone's toothless smile
spells out the letters: Roslin Castle,
illegible except for moss that's
encased each letter in a gumshield.

Makes me think of neanderthal shadow boxers,
those express trains with names of castles
and thunder-and-lightning carriages that we
counted past. The train-tracks have been taken up,
the path's a toothless cinder now, crackling
with infill underfoot. Paw-prints of heather,
gorse and broom. And an old crone's smile in velveteen.

DAMON'S ROSE

*"Here Damon lies whose Songs did sometime grace
The murmuring Esk. May Roses shade the place!"*

The poet's name is stamped
on his unmortared mausoleum;
an inscription of poetry
addressed to time not place, tied with
a sprig of alabaster roses;
a parcel without contents save
for flagstones and some gardenware
and tablets pink with harling;
no skull and crossbone stones to catch
the curio-collector's eye;
a pile of junk mail except for
that single rose whose living
loyalty seals dead Damon's show.

INN OF COURT

My cousin says I pronounce them wrong: Roslin,
Lasswade, emphasis is on the "ros", the "lass",
but I can only mouth them as a joke;
my tongue slips like my feet in the leaf-slurry,
lapses into its natural handedness.

If Drummond could be to me the sandstone that
rubs rubefacient on these Scotswood pines
as I amble round the grounds of Hawthornden,
bolt myself in at night with his wooden bar,
a battering ram retroactive into time.

Each day more rhododendrons have unflowered:
first, pink, then with a glorious transfusion
of ochre in the blood, vermilion red.
Today I discovered a Drummond's cave-carved
initials "W.D. 1716".

As I run my finger along the edge
of the W's two bisecting cuts,
instead of thrilling with a torque of red
my finger bears the smudge of talcumed stone.
Inside, the doors have writers' names

blazoned in black lettering on each panel.
Sitting before an empty page,
conjuring poems, making shadow soup,
I see my twelve letters painted on the door,
obscure remembrance in an inn of court.

Michael Henry.

Raymond Tong

DISASTER ZONE

During the first forty-eight hours
our television screens revealed
unforgettable scenes of devastation.
We had glimpses through the brown smoke
of a ruined landscape, vaguely reminiscent
of a battlefield from the First World War.
We saw the jagged remains of houses,
the roads engulfed with rubble and littered
with corpses. And once there were close-ups
of a ragged group of dazed and injured children,
apparently unattended and quietly whimpering.

On the third day we were informed
that further television coverage
of the situation in the Disaster Zone
would not be possible. No reason was given,
but a few hours later the radio
bulletins from the region also ceased.
People endeavouring to communicate
by telephone with friends and relatives

inside the Zone had already discovered
that all the lines were dead. It was thus
no longer possible to observe
the appalling desolation or to hear
the anguish of those pleading for assistance.

NECESSARY WORDS

"This is our country". At last the words
were uttered: four simple words my ancestors
would have spoken clearly with passion and pride.

Hesitating, I had only muttered them,
as though the words themselves were loathe to be heard,
were somehow strangely forbidden or else untrue.

I had been taught they were dangerous words,
words to be held in check, not to be used
in view of their likely effect on others.

And yet they are very necessary words:
as necessary to the English as to the Scots,
the Welsh, the Irish or the Japanese.

THE ARBITERS

Here there are no whips raised in anger,
no thought-criminals or thought-police,
only the feeling of being manipulated.

Here the blandly smiling arbiters decide
how to present the awkward and unacceptable,
what should be disclosed and what withheld.

Most of the media, unlike a Ministry
of Love, does not persuade us what to think,
but much more subtly, what not to think.

Seeking to help us find enlightened answers
they make omission an equalising virtue,
obscuring every subject deemed taboo.

LONG OVERDUE

Now that
the Democrats
have been born, is it not
time to have a Republican
party?

Raymond Tong.

Impressions of Morocco

Gillean Somerville

Had I been on my own I would never have found it. There were no signs, not even in Arabic. But Aziz's sisters were chaperoning me, thus placing me in a role I am not used to.

The taxi dropped us on one of the main streets in the European quarter of Fès, and Suraaya and Jamila made their way briskly up a narrow alleyway. We paid a man with a black moustache. He was just visible through a hole in a wall, barred with an iron grille. The entrance fee was 25 pence each. Across the alleyway was the back entrance to a bakery, a frequent adjunct to a *hammam*. The same woodfire, presumably, heats both water and oven. A group of men and boys hung round the doorway watching us, the men furtively, almost guiltily, the small boys blatantly, eyes wide with curiosity. I am a constant source of interest here, a European woman in a raincoat, the more so when accompanied by two young Moroccan girls in traditional *djellabahs*.

Once inside you are in another world. as if you had entered a convent. A bare room with a polished stone floor and grey plaster walls. Round the walls wooden slatted seating. Two small squares cut in the ceiling and fitted with wire-reinforced glass let in the sunlight, the only source of light there is. Behind a counter two hawk-eyed, ancient ladies, their faces dry and wrinkled as walnuts, their bodies swathed in layers of brightly coloured ankle-length dresses and knotted headsquares, take charge of bathers' possessions. From the inner chambers of the place, you hear constant exploding cacophonies of sound, echoing from wall to wall, as in any swimming-pool, only here the space is more confined, the voices solely female.

You strip down to your knickers, which they elegantly call your slip, bundle your belongings into a carrier-bag, or wrap them in a towel knotted in the middle, depending on your means or level of sophistication, and leave them with one of the hawk-eyed ladies. Don't expect hi-tech appurtenances, like lockers or coat-hooks. Don't even expect a mirror.

As nearly nude as makes no difference, therefore, and carrying only what you need for washing, you enter the bathing area. This consists of three large, bare rooms, swilling with water and hazy with steam, each one you enter being hotter than the one you leave behind. The scent of henna and the smell of orange peel linger in the air. You make first for the hottest room, after which you make your way back to the coolest room, the one nearest the exit.

Your first task is to search out a set of large plastic buckets. Usually three is enough, but if the session is crowded you may have to negotiate. You fill them with water from one of the two stone water tanks, one hot and one cold. The hot water is very hot. Then you lug each bucket to an appropriate area of free floor space, which becomes your 'territory' for the duration. If the session is crowded this can be difficult. Once you have laid claim to your space you scoop out water from your bucket to clear it of dirt from previous bathers - chunks of hair and strips of orange peel - before settling to wash. The streaming water escapes through drains strategically set in the tiled floor.

For Moroccans whose homes are not equipped with European-style bath-rooms, and even those who are, a visit to the *hammam* is a weekly, communally shared ritual. Aziz's sisters spend three hours in here at a time. They have been coming since they were toddlers hanging on to their mother's skirts. They are practical and well organised. Everything they need is in polythene bags, more efficient in the circumstances than my posh sponge-bag with its pretty flowers which gets soggy in no time on the steaming wet floor.

They have brought two specific local preparations with them. One is a soft black soap, the colour of treacle and the consistency of soft toffee, which is made, they tell me, from olives. The other is a shampoo called *rasul*, which they say is made from a mixture of stones, spices and shampoo. Stones? What sort of stones? Dry, as you see it on sale by the tubful in the *soukh*, it looks like chunks of dark grey earth. First, you lather yourself with the soap, leaving time for the impurities in your skin to rise to the surface, ready to be scrubbed away by a metallic glove. If you don't mind paying a bit more, you can get one of the attendants to do this for you, giving you an all-over glowing massage. This takes longer than it sounds if it is to be done properly. An hour, perhaps.

Moroccan women take great pride in their hair. The *Qu'ran* counsels them never to cut it because it is a gift of God. Aziz's sisters tell me that when their mother was young her hair fell to her ankles and was very beautiful. Grooming this crowning glory, consequently, takes a long time, a soothing, rhythmic ritual among the crowded steamy clamours of the *hammam*. You begin by mixing a little of the *rasul* with water, till it has the consistency of wet grey clay. Then you rub it evenly over your hair. Rinse and repeat. Then you comb your hair meticulously, being careful to direct it the way you will want it to be when it is dry. Otherwise, it will be tacky and unmanageable. Finally you burnish your hair with henna, to preserve its dark, seductive gleam.

I haven't the patience to engage in such time-consuming rituals. My way of life and temperament put the prospect of glamour firmly out of reach, but I am fascinated to observe the process. I finish my ablutions in a quarter of an hour, relief enough after a bathless week in this hot and dusty city, and then am free to sit back and watch.

It could be the erotic dream of a Victorian genre painter - all this abundant female flesh seen through a shifting veil of steam, the Sultan's scores of concubines preparing for his next visit, or a dim corner of Dante's *Inferno*, depending on your point of view. Caucasian male travellers to Arab countries usually enthuse about the *hammam*. Women are more circumspect. The Arabs certainly take the process very seriously. They have almost a mystic sense of the cleansing power of water and personal cleanliness is a sacred duty. They view European bathing habits with mild humour, bordering on pity or even contempt. I have a suspicion they may have a point, but am loath to surrender the comforts I have grown up with.

It surprises me how easily these women wear their nakedness in each other's company. Outside they are swathed head to foot in their haiks and djellabahs and many of the older women still wear veils. Only a minority, the rich, wear European clothes. In the seclusion of the *hammam*, however, they shed their self-consciousness.

Young Moroccan girls are usually slim and beautiful and carry themselves

Photograph, 'Rendezvous, Essaouira' by Owen Logan
from Al Maghirib: Photographs of Morocco (Polygon & Third Eye Centre)

with a cool serenity. It may be a mask, it is certainly conditioned, but it is impressive nonetheless. Most older women soon put on weight but don't seem to consider this a tragedy. Their men don't like scrawny wives. A good armful consoles a man for much material poverty. Arab women are not so bombarded as western women are with glossy images of unrealisable beauty. Nor have they evolved to post-feminist notions of fitness and diet. They are as they are. They may put great hefty lumps of sugar in their tea, but they habitually eat fresh fruit and vegetables, pulses, white meat and fish. And for ordinary women, lacking labour-saving devices in the home, housework is hard physical labour. So, whether they bulge like Buddhas or droop with dried-out breasts in age, and many have bellies marked with white caesarean scars, they don't seem to mind. Their religion, after all, counsels resignation.

They gossip endlessly as they wash. News travels here faster and more reliably by word of mouth, *le téléphone arabe*, than by any other means. Too much elsewhere is censored. Violent arguments can break out over the temporary ownership of buckets. I witnessed a desperate tug-of-war between two large, ungainly young women slipping and sliding on the treacherously wet floor. It was viewed as good entertainment and seemed to leave no hard feelings. If they can defuse tension by laughter they will. They hate sulking. It's a counter-productive emotion, a pointless self-indulgence.

I wonder what the little boys make of it all, gazing round in silent awe, in between scrubbing sessions at their mothers' hands. When a cascade of wailing descends you may be sure it's a young boy having his hair shampooed. Girls are expected to behave better. A recent winner of the *Prix Goncourt*, the Moroccan francophone writer, Tahar ben Jelloun, has written of his own impressions of being taken as a small boy to the women's *hammam* in his novel of Fès, *Harrouda*, and the charged erotic fantasies it filled him with. About the age of five boys stop going to the women's *hammam* and accompany their fathers to the men's.

When I come out I feel exhausted. I wrap my towel round me and sink on to a space on the slatted wooden benches in the entrance hall, totally lethargic. Not that violent activity is advised. Nor is pouring gallons of ice cold Coca Cola down your throat. Take it easy. Come round gently. A little water, perhaps, or a glass of mint tea. Otherwise you pay for it later, as I have done, bent double over yet another plastic bucket at home, retching till the relentless seizure passes.

TURKEY ON THE ROOF

Mostly it crouched there, folded in its shiny black feathers, like an ancient dowager in a ball-dress sitting out a dance. It conserved its energy with remorseless dignity, a fastidiousness of manner emphasising its sense of superior breeding. Its eyes, as it blinked, glinted in the sunlight, suggesting an intelligence not easily fooled. It knew what it was there for, tied by a leg to a heavy wooden ladder on the flat rooftop of a modest Arab house in Fès. The ugliness of those wrinkled red wattles ruffing its long neck seemed an additional humiliation. It bore both with noble resignation.

Occasionally it got up and stalked about tentatively, exploring the limits of its freedom, pecking at the scattered grains the children had left for it or taking sips of water from a grubby pink plastic bowl. Karim is merciful. At first he had left the bird free, but being called down to the shop for several minutes one morning had returned to find it poised on the parapet, about to stretch its inappropriate wings in flight. That couldn't happen again. So the ladder had been laid down. He had given it a fair latitude of string, but even so it could not wander far. There were times, however, when its longing would overwhelm it, and it would suddenly erupt, heaving itself upwards in an ungainly lunge, lashing out with a desperate flurry of wings. The ladder would rattle and clatter as the bird tried to drag it across the concrete floor. In the intensity of its passion, it looked as if it might break a leg in the struggle, but it seemed to have an instinct as to how far it could safely go. Its futile protest made, it would subside at last like a punctured tyre and, drawing its head beneath that ugly flap of skin, reconcile itself to its bitter lot.

Karim and I bought it in the Bab Ftuah poultry market on the perimeter of Fès Medina. As the date of the *Fête du Trône* approaches, the annual celebration in March of the King's accession, so the price of poultry increases. The thing is to get in early. Even a week before, the market is busy. We passed shops filled with scores of chittering white chickens cooped up in pens, guarded by their keepers, lounging about with an air of jaded cynicism. But the birds we were interested in, along with the ducks, geese, hens and gaudy-plumaged cockerels, sat docilely in tethered rows along one side of the street. Their keepers were mostly old men from the countryside, wearing turbans and heavy wool *djellabahs*. Their gnarled and wrinkled faces were tanned to a leathery toughness and they assessed potential customers with shrewdly mischievous eyes. They gave no impression of being in any hurry to clinch a deal. If your offer was absurdly low they would grin wordlessly through the large gaps in their surviving teeth, where here and there a gold cap gleamed like a secret treasure. The younger men, dressed in shabby European clothes, were more restless, their manners nervous, their expressions haunted. They were quicker to push forward and readier to conclude a sale.

Karim started with some preliminary skirmishing, exclaiming in disbelief at the prices. Then he withdrew to consider, twirling his moustache and chewing his way through a small screw of roasted peanuts, purchased on impulse from a nearby street vendor.

"What do you think?" he asked.

What did *I* think? An image swam into my mind of a supermarket counter, white, ice-cool, swept clean of dust, on which lay rows of identical packages, each containing a scrupulously weighed and priced allocation of bluish, goose-pimpled flesh, already killed, plucked and trussed, drumsticks presenting arms on white polystyrene trays, vacuum-wrapped in cling film.

He passed me two birds to test for weight. I held them awkwardly by the feet, wary of the strong thrust of life still in them.

"I've no idea," I said at last. "I've never bought a *live* bird before!"

We settled for a solid, energetic-looking bird, which cost us the equivalent of £8-9. The next problem was how to get it home. We were too far away to walk, with or without a struggling turkey, and not on a direct bus route. We had come by taxi, but the first few taxi-drivers we approached gave us a wide berth. "*C'est l'heure pour dîner, non?*" said one, abandoning his vehicle to take a quick pee, leaving us in no doubt he hoped we would be gone on his return. One or two others simply started up their engines and drove off before we could even ask. The next was not so lucky. He was talking to a friend when Karim shoved me in the back and laid claim to the front passenger seat. There was a moment of suspense when the driver suddenly realised what had happened. OK, he agreed reluctantly, provided the bird didn't disgrace itself.

It didn't. Breeding tells.

The rooftop substitutes for a garden in a modest Arab urban house. Here the women do the family washing in a stone washtub and take what exercise their comparatively restricted lives permit them. Here the vegetables are stored and family pets are kept. Here, too, the livestock bought for food, the sacrificial lamb for *Aid El Kebir* or for a child's baptism, a fowl for fattening, and the turkey for the *Fête du Trône* are tethered until the day of execution.

It's a peaceful place, the rooftop, fenced in from and high above the intrusions of the outside world. Here ubiquitous television aerials rake the sky. Scarely a home is without one. A few blocks away rises the solid square tower of the local mosque, its walls covered with gleaming new white and green tiles. Five times a day, regular as clockwork from dawn till dusk, comes the sonorous call to prayer. Through an alleyway opposite you can see a shanty town straggling up a hillslope that was once an olive-grove. Morocco is now experiencing the flight of the rural poor to the cities in search of work and all the concomitant social ills of such a population shift. Beyond that a distant undulation of dry sandy hills shuts out the horizon.

Down in the dusty street below Karim plays football with his friends. Eager Maradonas of the back streets, they follow the fortunes of the game with an obsessional interest. It feeds their secret dreams. This is the sort of area that fills the immigrant ghettoes of Europe. Next door a fig-tree grows unchecked in the courtyard of a one-storey dwelling, untended and shut up for years while its owner makes a living for himself in the south of France.

There is always something going on in the street. In the morning there is the rubbish collector with his donkey cart and various street hawkers selling eggs, fruit and vegetables. Junk collectors appear, too. Then there is always the postman, often bringing eagerly awaited news of sons and daughters in Europe. Then there are the chants of small children penned inside the local Koranic school. They emerge in a rush at lunchtime, carrying their plastic satchels and their slates, often neat little French-style overalls disguising the poverty of their ordinary clothes. Sometimes there will be the joyful ululations of a wedding party or the mournful male dirge accompanying a funeral procession. Very occasionally there is something more exciting, like the sudden incursion of *gnaoui* dancers, swart men with pigtails from the desert towns of the south, who leap frenetically to the hypnotic beat of an accompanying drum and bring everyone to the rooftops to watch.

In the evening Karim comes up to the rooftop for a quiet smoke. He is thin and slightly stooped, signs both of poverty and submission to inconsequence. If it's hot he'll change out of his shabby, well-darned European clothes into a loose black cotton *gandoura*, better suited to the climate, and a pair of the flat, soft leather shoes with pointed toes which you buy in the *soukh*.

"It's beautiful," I said one evening as we leaned on the parapet and the setting sun trailed a purple shadow across the hills.

He spat out a faint sliver of tobacco.

"No," he replied, "it's not beautiful here. In France it's beautiful. Here everyone is poor."

We talk sometimes, but without much conviction, about the possibilities of escape. He has his job and his family here. He needs both. What would life in Europe bring him now?

There is a frantic flurry behind us and the rattle of wood against concrete. The turkey is engaged in one of its last spasmodic bids for freedom. Tomorrow is the day of its demise. We watch its brief struggle dispassionately.

"It can't escape its destiny," I say.

Karim chucks his cigarette butt to the ground and grinds it flat with his heel. "That bird leaves its shit everywhere," he snaps.

A shiver of wind billows out his *gandoura*. Our arms are showing goose-pimples. We go down into the body of the house.

Gillean Somerville

:Photograph of Morocco by Owen Logan

Taban Lo Liyong

TYPING LESSONS

The quick brown fox
Jumped over the lazy black fox
    (that doesn't sound right!)

The quick white fox
Jumped over the lazy brown fox
    (that's even worse!)

The quick black fox
Jumped over hurdles in Seoul
    (that's better.)

COME, SIT WITH ME MY LOVE IN VIDEOLAND

Come, sit with me my love, in Videoland
Where love lives, cares are taken away
And for a pound or two one enters another world
Where beautiful girls are laid before the hour is over
Where handsome men are kissed red-eyed before long
Where karate experts demolish evil men
Where James Bond proves the British are still top
Where Indian love songs and sentiments bring tears
Where cars move so fast, police can't catch them
Where planes, trains, ships, helicopters
Are all deployed before the story is over . . .

Before the story is over
    characters have changed clothes ten times
    have struck one another, been kissed, and drunk

Before the story is over
    beautiful cousins have become wived with child
    and either become tougher or very old and poor

Before the story is over
    if the characters are ugly, rough, and dirty
    expect bloodletting, tongue bursting a rape or two

Before the hour is over
    if Chinese are involved, there is karate, cockfight
    a lot of jumping up and down with swords

Before the hour is over
    American college girls have left homework
    stripped naked and made love to boy, girl, or self

Before the hour is over
    American prison scenes will display kings and queens
    homosexual love encouraged to demoralise stalwarts

Before the hour is over
    one learns a few things
    with films of sex, there won't be much to imagine
    the girls will deliver, in all sorts of contortions
    the boys will also deliver in any hole
    and lots of grunting noise will be made ending in *Das Gut.*

Come then, away my love
Let's go and look for a secret place
And do as they do in Videoland
The next American girl I meet had better watchout!

LAMENT FOR YOUNGER BROTHER BORN TOO LATE

The major themes are already covered
Better deal with sub-themes now
Or you'll eat your heart out
Since you were born after heroic days were over.

At decolonisation you were a pup
If your father did not participate
Blame your genes for it
Look for other things to do.

Negritude was fashioned by Sedar Senghor
Criticised to death by Oluwole Soyinka.
Go socialistic, realistic, modernistic
Or post-post modernistic to be there first.

How Europe underdeveloped Africa is old stuff
Walter Rodney left it behind, went and died in Guyana . . .
Perhaps macro-economics, small or black is beautiful.
Bismarck or Old Man of Europe are more insightful?
Proverbs are done to death by Achebe, Clark and the rest
Perhaps Brecht, Blake, Shaw and Nietzsche;
Pharaonic Egypt, China, Red India could provide new figures of speech
With which to fix modern times conclusively and intricably well?

It is tragic to be born too late
After the main events are done with
Especially when you're blind enough
To think yours is not heroic

THE COWS OF SHAMBAT

The cows of Shambat are yellow in the morning
And gradually turn to dull grey by night.
They feed on sawdust, high jumps and bats;
Are fertilised by ink, pollen, and rebuffs
Giving us that quintessential mixed breed
That is neither beast, bird, grain nor fish.

The Roman sage had jested; out of Africa
Expect hell let loose and disjambments;
The ancient cartographers had conjectured
All kinds of beasts to fill Afric's vast expanse.
To prove all these and other stupidness true
Shambat jumps to the rescue.

When the season of folly is on
They repair to their secluded upper theatre
Throw known common Elements on the crucible
Pour the conjuror's brew on the species
- Intent to manufacture angels or worse -
Turn the gas on, and in rapid succession
There are contortions of limbs, sizzling of flesh,
Loud explosions and blinding flying sparks.
        Then there is utter blankness.
Bedazzled by the results of their exertions
- Like the proverbial bull in a china shop -
They emerge
Sweating
groping
hobbling
   down
        the
        stairs
On three legs.
Taban Lo Liyong (Sudan)

Fleur Adcock

A DREAM

We watched for the great cremation.
The governors loved it.
They'd concealed all the treasures -
money and the next world -
in that enemy's arms.

It never came about.
A different heat happened.

We ourselves hired
the angels of dissolution,
the invisible munching host.

Here's the other sight -
slate-grey as far as the horizon.
Where can it have fallen from?
It didn't fall. It melted:
torrents of ice and salt, our gross Jacuzzi.

MARGARET NEEDHAM

Their cottages were built of mud and straw,
but they had a stone church to be wed in

So this particular young spinster,
Margaret Needham of the parish of Syston,

walked there to marry Joseph Bilson
on the 6th of February 1696

(or 1697 by our calendar,
now they've trimmed the years to end in December.)

And if she was 23, the daughter of Joseph
and Mary (or possibly Margaret) Needham,

she'll do, I suppose. But if she was the other one -
seventeen and a half or a little more,

baptized in 1679, 'daughter
of William Needham by his wife Helena' -

she sits a fraction closer to my heartbeat
in the bloodstream that runs from her to me:

I was once a teenage bride myself
(and, like Margaret, not even pregnant.)

This young one has my favour too, I admit,
for her mother's sake. I fancy a Helena,

the name of a Byzantine empress-saint,
pinned to the topmost twig of our family tree:

a just-not-quite incongruous ornament
above all the Elizabeths and Marys

to twinkle out over their homely shades,
their harsh lives, with a frail persistent glitter.

Fleur Adcock (New Zealand)

Standard Language, Rigid Minds
William Neill

Some painters still mix their own colours. I cannot imagine any such artist abandoning a worthwhile process simply because it had been used by Van Eyck, or a pianist refusing to accompany a recorder on the grounds that the concert flute had replaced its orchestral use. It seems, however, that in the great world of literature, there are those who throw out words for even flimsier reasons. There is in fact a kind of critic who objects to the work of poets on the grounds that they use words which are slang, dialect, not standard speech, made-up or otherwise objectionable. There have always been critics who tried to turn the whole flood of literature into the piddling stream of which they, personally, approved. There are even metropolitan reviewers who seem to think that the only valid writing emanates from London, the Home Counties, and Overseas, a kind of imperial preference surviving from the days of the Raj. It is not surprising that writers beyond the Thames Valley Pale should find this irritating: what is surprising is that alleged purveyors of *Scottish critical opinion* should ally themselves to such a narrowly provincial viewpoint. A study of that nation from whom the expression 'beyond the Pale' originated shows quite clearly that posterity considered the poets beyond the Pale the more remarkable. It is worth noting that Henrysoun and Dunbar, despite their northern form of 'Inglis' were considered by G S Fraser to be superior to any English poet of that age. Had they been born in this day, they might well have been ignored on purely geographical grounds.

Parochialism of this kind is not new. Wordsworth read to London audiences who sniggered at his Cumberland accent instead of listening to his poetry, although the Cockney accent of Keats may well have passed muster in an age before Daniel Jones. Burns was continually advised by the Scottish literary cognoscenti to write in English if he wished to gain great repute. Lessons to be drawn from this ought surely to have taught the poets of today that strict orthodoxy (whatever its devotees imagine that to mean) in allophone or lexis should be avoided like the plague. The histories of Herodotus, the poetry of Homer and the Gospels are all written in a Greek not spoken in Athens: all have stayed in print for some considerable time.

Yet it seems that there are still those who have not learned their lesson. Articles appear from time to time which castigate novels and poetry on the ground that they use *archaisms*. Just when does a word become an archaism anyway? The definition on this island might be: as soon as some London reviewer says so. Does this sort of thing all stem from injudicious prattle about 'a man talking to men' and other remarks about bringing 'realism' into poetry? What exactly is meant by 'everyday language in poetry'? Language is a very specialised thing; it has many registers. The conditions on the back of a railway ticket are not written in the language appropriate to poetry, although there are some editors of anthologies who might be tempted to include them were they suitably carved up into lines by a poet of whom they approved. As soon as poetry becomes *genuine* 'everyday' language it ceases to be poetry. This is not to say that poetry cannot be written in colloquial language; it very often is, but if it is recognisably poetry it is not 'real' in the sense that *ordinary* everyday language is real. It is straining the reader's patience to make such an obvious point, but in these days of muddled thinking by reviewers et al, it certainly needs to be said. Poetry is *heightened* language. Poetry can also be filled to the brim with archaisms, borrowings, foreign words, new words, made-up words, dialect words, slang words . . . and all sorts of assorted phonemes. Anyone who cannot see this ought to go back and read Shakespeare, or Joyce. One wonders if the critics who carp about which of the few coins in their little purse of words we shall use have in fact taken benefit from any reading at all. Shakespeare muddles up the English use of 'shall' and 'will'. His pronunciation of English was quite violently different from Chaucer's and divided by the same large gap from the RP accents in which, until a few years ago, it was thought fitting to read him. He uses what were, in his own day, archaisms like 'kneen' for 'knees' and 'eyen' for 'eyes'. (The variant 'een' is still in use all over Scotland where it is certainly NOT an archaism.) He uses forms like 'honester' and 'violentest' which would doubtless gain the Highers student a red underline despite a protest backed by the Shakespearean canon. He invented words, borrowed words from other tongues and made up other phrases unique in his time which have become modern cliches. Joyce's *Finnegan's Wake* is an example of the same desire to play with words and phrases from all quarters. Why then should one attack the late Hugh MacDiarmid, no longer able to defend himself against such snipings, for doing just the same thing in Scots? This seems to me to be simply another example of 'the Scottish cringe'. MacDiarmid is being 'too Scottish' - so we will throw this baby out with the bath water - like almost everything else. Don't let us talk about tartan and bagpipes, not because these have become monotonous stereotypes, but because the Thames Valley Establishment will use them to poke fun at us.

What exactly to we mean by 'English'? I have of late started to call the English language the *lingua franca* for no other reason than that I find the term 'English' obfuscatory. Even in its Old English days it was not merely the tongue of Angles and Saxons. People of Celtic origin spoke it also . . . the poet Caedmon, for instance; nor was it then, any more than today, a fixed canon, a fact that naive language 'purists' seem unable to assimilate. Constructions which fifty years ago would have been regarded as solecisms are now accepted by the linguistic 'establishment'. One of the remaining case-endings of English is now in the process of disappearing: the relative pronoun 'whom'. In this century English has become the equivalent of the Greek *koine* of mediaeval Latin. It is used by many different languages for international communication. But there are also many variants of English: Australian, South African, West Indian, East Indian and - the major voice - American. These are proof against Thames Valley *folie de grandeur* despite anything the media may say or think. Americans are not going to stop putting the word 'gotten' into verses because some ill-educated London reviewer does not like it. If you want royalties galore (a good Gaelic word) aim for America, not London, and write good American soap operas.

Despite the burden of establishment antipathy, Scots and Gaelic poets continue to appear: there are still people who do speak these tongues; monoglot attempts to kill them off in favour of some absolute, fixed, 'standard English' which can only happen when English is as completely fossilised, like classical-period Greek or Latin, have failed under the impact of much excellent poetry in both languages. Poetry is still being written in our indigenous tongues for all the misguided sneers of those who know neither, but seem to gain a media platform on very slim grounds.

Fifty years ago it was regarded as 'common' to speak either Scots or Gaelic. Nowadays there is a kind of snob charisma around Gaelic while Scots continues, at one level or another, to be looked upon as vulgar. One often gets the feeling that alleged critics of Scottish literature who affect to despise the old language are motivated more by snobbery than literary concerns. The accepted pundits say things like . . . 'of course Scots was already dying in Burns' time'. This is arrant nonsense. Scots was far from dead in my own boyhood Ayrshire. Scots is far from dead in the area in which this article is being written. Gaelic and Scots are both excellent media through which to read poetry because they still have a kind of freshness that standard English (I except the English 'dialects') is rapidly losing as far as the poetic voice is concerned. Modern usages of what Garioch called 'hen-hoose noises: uckin-uckin' are back in fashion. Chaucer's 'erses' and 'queynts' have been refurbished for modern use although the excellence of his metrics appears to be despised by our modern verslibrateurs. Even Larkin could not resist it. It is ironic that some appear to see these grand old words as giving a 'modern' flavour to their lines. The basic feeling behind this extended use of the sexual and scatological word-hoard is not so much a desire in the writers to shock their grannies (who knew the words before they were born) as to give a tired language a short burst of lexical adrenalin. Scots, on the other hand, is so vigorous a tongue that it does not need this intravenous *nostalgie de la boue* though words such as 'aidle' and 'sharn' show the Scottish repertoire to be superior in the cloacal word-chest. That Scots is still robust enough and fresh enough to produce great poetry must be obvious to anyone with an ear. That MacDiarmid's revitalised Scots contains sustained passages of much beauty is obvious to any true poet and those who cannot hear the music should not claim to expertise in such matters.

One of the favourite ways of knocking Scots, used a great deal by such as have demonstrated their inability to use it, is to consign all poetry written in that tongue to what they are pleased to call the Kailyard. An expression first invented by Henley to debunk a group of sentimental rural writers is now used in a false context to condemn any rural writing in Scots. Nowadays the best Scots is spoken in rural areas and many writers in Scots live in such areas. Their work is usually a great deal less sentimental than the urban girnings of city poets writing in the establishment language to air their own synthetic *angst*. That good, hard writing in Scots is condemned as 'Kailyard' by writers ignorant of the origin of that term argues more for their obtuseness than their literary awareness. Presumably such critics would describe Hesiod's *Works and Days* or Virgil's *Georgics* as 'Kailyard'.

Much of the splenetic comment anent MacDiarmid (and other symbols of unrelenting Scottishness) seems to me to be rooted in the desire to toady to the London book market. Of course, getting poetry published is difficult enough without compounding the problems by writing in Scots, or Gaelic. But this is not a poetry problem, it is a marketing problem. Anyone who writes for the market ought to abandon the poetry field forthwith. If on the other hand a decision is made that poetry is the target to aim at, then such mercenary ploys should be abandoned. I am not saying that one should welcome the kind of foolish disregard given to Emily Dickinson by her contemporary critics. Most poets want to be read. But surely a run of two hundred (like Eliot's *Waste Land*) has a literary value beyond ten thousand volumes of mediocre maunderings aimed specifically at a lucrative market. The fact that nowadays most good poetry is in the first instance put out by small, brave publishers on a shoe-string budget ought to be a matter of shame to those well-heeled firms too mean to take the chance of losing what to them is, to use American, peanuts.

To write in Scots (or Gaelic) whether synchronic or 'plastic', whether colloquial or 'reconstituted', pure or macaronic, is neither a jingoistic harking-back, nor a bathetic nostalgia for Maclaren's Kailyard, but a genuine desire to find a strong poetic language which has deep relevance for the Scottish psyche. That there are young, forward-looking poets sufficiently aware of this and willing to carry on in the face of criticism by their elders (but not necessarily their betters) says much for the example set by the late MacDiarmid, George Campbell Hay, Robert Garioch and others whose work in native tongues will surely outlast that of their detractors. Notably none of these confined their work solely to indigenous tongues. They were all fine poets in standard English and the much-undervalued George Campbell Hay in all three languages.

A preference for poetry in standard English is not to be decried: to couple this choice with the denial of poetic validity to Scots, whether of MacDiarmid or any other, sounds more like simple malice than fair comment. To make one young Scottish writer lay down his pen because he feels inhibited, not by his own tongue, but by a despair induced by the sneers of those who care nothing for Scots and less for Gaelic (whatever their lip-service) does not make such critics the servants of literature. It indicates a slavery to their own unexamined prejudice.

William Hershaw

The Caring Co-op Poetry Festival 1989
*Entries may be in English or Ethnic Community languages.

I will scrieve o summer . . .

I will mak a poem oot o summerlicht,
Ti mind it, ti haud its gowden hours
In ma ain words, ti mak sense and form
O a sairness felt, o a brawness, deed
As ma ain dwynin dreams and life ti be.
Where the sky hangs high, all blue,
Whaur blae hings the carry, the laverock's lift,
I will unmak and remak it aw aince mair . . .

I was born in 1957 when television was becoming affordable to the working classes. Later, inspired by Burns and McDiarmid, I wanted to write poems in Scots but my confidence had been undermined by my education and my exposure to an alien English culture. I thought I didn't know sufficient Scottish words and that even if I tried the outcome would be a highly artificial verse that the Lallans experts would laugh at. I thought I was lacking in the linguistic roots and cultural credibility to write in the way I thought and spoke. It did not occur to me either that poetry is a selective and highly organised form of language which even in the guise of a spontaneous outpouring is in a sense artificial . . .

Oot ben whaur the sewage pipe
Skails pizen til the fleean watters
Summertime has cam at Seaforthside.
Prawn-pink, the coal-flaucht sands are croodit
Oot wi human emerteens that streetch oot til the Black Rock.
The High Street is loupin tae -
Thrang ootby the tuim and clarty shelves
O the disused Co-op Drapery Dep.
A faimly fae Glesgi tak up the hale braidth o the causey . . .

By starting to write in Scots I may still have been producing murder-poetry or even murdering poetry but I no longer felt uneasy about the results. I instantly realised my previous efforts had not connected with life and had therefore not been poetry at all. I had been posing with words and playing with techniques at the expense of making. As the first in the family to attend a university I had been conscious of the distance this created between us - noo I turned back til ma faimly, ma bairnhood, ti celebrate the fowk an the airt I cam frae. I thocht o twa grandfaithers graftin their life doon the Pit and fund scrievin Scots mair easy nor shovelin snaw aff a dyke - and bi faur easier than puin yer sark aff at a pairty whiles keepin yer jersey on . . .

Haw Maw! Ah want ti gan oan the ferr!
Haw Gran - Can we no gan fir chips? Jason!
You juist haud yer wheesht an keep still
Till yer faither cams oot o the bookies, Charlene!
Step oot o thon dug's dirt, Jesus,
Ah'll murder these weans so Ah wull,
Whaur is thon stupit big lump?
The auld Bin Hill tilts a faitherlie broo
Til the blae lift . . .

Gin ye scrieve in Scots ye maun expect yer darg ti be ignored whiles gin ye nip their heids eneuch they'll mibbe pay ye the compliment o makkin a fuil o ye in a fower line review. A wheen o cliched girns aboot Scots heeze up mair aften than weeds eftir rain; the leid is deean; it cannae cam ti greips wi the new technology; its scrievers dinnae bide in the real world; Scots has nivir groun up as a leid; pawky blethers aboot agrarian bairnhoods are aw it's fit for; ye cannae scrieve prose in Scots. Makers dinnae heed sic threips - ca a Lumphinnans Arts Renaissance syne daur the warld ti refute it. Ye can pruve the contrarie o their bletherin bi juist daein it. Scots is ay in the predicament o Irish in the young days o Yeats - snirtit at by colonists and colonised alike. Ken yer enemy and expect nae help or intelligent criticism. A dumbfounderin thocht is that the muckle rubbish ye hear aboot Scots has been speyed sin Burns was a bairn. The leid isnae deean, juist changin, so heave awa . . .

Hopkins, Blake and Davie Lindsay stecher oot the Novar Bar
As the deean sun skails bluid-licht ower bi Kinghorn.
The lift wynds back ti bairndays in Cowdenbeath;
The Moss burns reid and reeky
An through the smoke I speir a claes-horse tent,
Lucky-totties, Store ice-lollies, juice and Gala-days.
The stoury roads atween the burnin Moss
Tyave doon ti Burntisland Shows -
In the het and dizzy birlin air a hundred thochts
Swim widdershins like tadpoles in a jeely-jar.
Spier Truth gleesh in the watter . . .

Let nae mood gan ben athoot scrievin it doon - a
truthfu and thochtfu accoont is a poem . . .

The Poem (entries may not exceed 40 lines in length).

Blae hings the lift abune bairns' green laughter -
For summer's a lang while ti play
At hide-and-seek 'mang a leaf-happit wigwam,
Wyndin a game through the wuids aw day.

Seevin weeks loused fae the shuil or mibbe
Wuid-elves croonin an eldrich sang
Or bairn-ghaists o the auld Bin Village
Singan o summers lang gan.

The Glossary (to an imaginary poem).

Scouth	- Freedom of movement
Screeve	- Scrape a bow over fiddle strings
Screel	- Scream
Screenge	- Fish the sea bottom, inshore
Scriddan	- A mountain stream
Scrieve	- Write, shape, make
Scrift	- A long account
Scranch	- Grind the teeth
Scrim	- Strike vigorously
Screevie	- A slate pencil
Scriever	- derogative, A scribbler
Scotland	- Scouth
Alba	- Scriddan
England	- Scranch
Tory	- Scrim
History	- Scrift
Literature	- Screevie
Me	- Scriever
Song	- Screeve
Future	- Scrieve
Primal	- Screel
Dictionary	- Wurdbuik
Trawl	- Screenge

The faimly fae Glesgi gan on ti seek their faither,
Walk oot o ma tomorrows - they hae waukened the seed
O aw ma summers past, a future hairst ti be mindit . . .

*The Footnote.

The Binn Village was an isolated community situated half way up the Bin Hill behind Burntisland. The villagers, lacking electricity and sundry modern day comforts, made a living producing shale oil. By the early fifties all the occupants had left. (See *Fife - From Kirkcaldy To Kincardine* by John D MacDonald)

Yet I hae a footnote left . . .
*On the use of footnotes . . .
Since the publication of *Fower Brigs Ti A Kinrik*, there has been much critical discussion concerning the use of footnotes in poetry. Belgravio Fettes de Fettes complains that such items 'explain away' THE POEM, thus ruining its intrinsic POETIC qualities. Professor Henry Hurlygush sees such devices as no more than 'a self-conscious parade of erudition . . .'

William Hershaw

Phoebe Searched Dreams for a Green House in Brockley Rise

John Lyons

Phoebe's irritation was mounting. Thelma was late again. Every Friday Phoebe and Thelma met at Fellini's Café for a snack before going on to the Odeon Cinema. Usually Phoebe arrived around 4.30 and invariably had to wait, sometimes for up to 45 minutes before Thelma put in an appearance.

She was sitting in her customary place near the Café window, her back polishing the wallpaper whose glory, like her patience, had faded away. From time to time she looked expectantly at the door and sucked her teeth, making that characteristic sound that expresses exasperation.

At last Thelma breezed in, her face split in an over-generous grin. "Oh Gord, Phoebe, there you are; I was fraid you gone. One of these days I sure you go lose your patience and go away."

Secretly, Phoebe was overjoyed and relieved, as she always was, to see Thelma; but she disguised her feelings with a dignified silence, staring at an imaginary object of great interest just off the side of her friend's head. Thelma had grown used to this little game. She took no notice and launched into yet another explanation for her late arrival. "Is that boss of mine again." Her grin contracted to a tight expression of annoyance. "He always giving me somethin to do at the last minute. I tell 'im I meeting a frien; and you know what that baccra Johnny with he brassface wanted to know? If I was meeting another man! I ask you! The cheek of some people."

Phoebe, who felt that her little game of silence had gone far enough to make her point without provoking a dispute, came in at this point.

"Well," she said, "he must like you a lot."

"Like!" Arms akimbo, eyebrows raised. "You know what that son-of-a-crapaud want, but I tellin you, I not that kind-a-woman."

Phoebe gave her friend one of her penetrating looks, knew that she was not telling the whole of the story, but didn't pursue that direction of conversation. "Let we get something to drink and listen to my latest dream. It is really, really strange. They getting me down these damn dreams."

Thelma bustled up to the counter for two mugs of hot chocolate and pieces of Enrico Fellini's soggy apple tart. Phoebe could see Enrico's eyes glued to Thelma's ample bosom and could hear her playful bantering which ended in her usual high-pitched laugh.

She returned triumphantly with two generous helpings of apple tart. "You goin to get yourself into trouble one of these days." Phoebe observed.

"Never. I doin no harm, and besides, the man got a wife as fierce as a hen setting on eggs."

Thelma sat down. She poured spilled chocolate from the saucer back into her cup. "Well, what you dream this time?"

For a few seconds Phoebe gave Thelma a steady look. "You never take my dreams seriously. They must mean something, you know. Anyway, I don't have to tell you if you not interested."

"Don't be so touchy, Phoebe. Course I interested."

For a moment Phoebe looked as though she was reconsidering whether or not she should relate her dreams to her friend.

"Well?" said Thelma, showing a considered interest.

"Oh Jesus, Thelma." Phoebe's eyes were springs of tears. "What do I do wrong to keep having these strange dreams night after night after night."

Thelma was lost for words. It was the first time that Phoebe was showing such feelings about her dreams. She drew her chair nearer to Phoebe's and put her arm around her shoulders. "Come on, Phoebe, don't get upset; they only dreams."

Phoebe pulled out a small, crumpled handkerchief from her pocket and blew her nose discreetly, looking uneasily around the cafe as she did so. "It was like this. I dream I was in my little garden behind the fowl-run back home in Trinidad planting peas and corn. It was a hot, hot day with the sun blazing down with a white light which seemed to bleach out all the colours around me. It was very, very strange. However, I bend down and started pushing me cutlass in the ground and dropping three corn grain and three peas in the hole. I straighten me back for a moment to rest, when all of a sudden me dead dog, Toby . . . remember Toby? Remember how Mr Mills, who I used to work for, kill 'im by accident backing his car out of his garage? Remember I wrote to you about it?"

Thelma did not remember. When she left Trinidad, six years ago, Phoebe did not have a dog. She had talked often enough about getting one; Thelma remembered that much. "No, Phoebe," a hint of impatience in her voice, "I can't remember."

Phoebe gave her a steady look. "You interested? Tell me if you want me to go on."

"Yes, Phoebe, I really want to hear all about your dream."

"Well, as I was saying, Toby suddenly appear; but instead of coming up to me and wagging his tail, as he used to when he was alive, he put his big black head in the air and started to howl, just as dogs go when somebody dead. I call 'im, 'Toby, Toby, come here boy,' but he just disappear, 'Pufff', just like that." She snapped her fingers.

"Anyway," she continued, "I was frighten, but somehow I went back planting corn and peas. Thelma you not going to believe this; when I push the cutlass in the ground, it started to bleed. Blood started to run everywhere I dig with me cutlass. I try to scream; I open me mouth wide but no sound come out. I tellin you, Thelma, it was one hell-of-a-frightening situation. I start to run round like a mad woman. Suddenly, I was no longer in me garden but in a canefield some place near Caroni. I was still running, crashing down all the cane in front me. I was running for how long I don't know.

All of a sudden, Mr Mills, my old boss in Trinidad, come out of the ground and is standing in front of me stark naked as the day he was born. Girl, I tellin you this time you could hear me scream all over Trinidad. I turn round and run in another direction, when suddenly he was in front of me again, barring me way. He had an odd expression on his face; he was sort of frowning and grinning at the same time. I start to back away from him when another strange thing happen: he turn into a carnival Lucifer with a Lucifer mask, bigger than normal with horns and all. He was holding a book in the shape of a coffin in one hand and pointing with his long Lucifer fingernails at something write down in it. And all the time he jerking up he body in front of me in a rude way. It was at this point in the dream that the scene change and I find myself sitting in a classroom with a lot of little children. Mr Arundel, my old Englishman teacher in elementary school, was pointing at the blackboard with his cane. On the blackboard was the words: 'They'll always be an England.' Then Shango drums started to beat and I wake up suddenly to hear Ethel, my landlady, banging on my door, trying to wake me up to go and look for work."

For a few seconds the two friends stared at each other without saying anything. It was Thelma who spoke first. "Girl, that was some dream."

"I tellin you Thelma, I getting tired, tired of these dreams. Now I even fraid to go to sleep at nights."

"What I find interesting is them two Englishmen who always in your dreams; Mr Mills who you used to work for as a maidservant, and Mr Arundel you old elementary school teacher, who liked teaching history so much."

A momentary silence passed over the two friends like a balmy breeze on a troubled day.

"You know, I never used to have these dreams in Trinidad, not even when Mervin drop me for that doogla (Mixed race, usually Indian and Negro) girl from Cocorite. But I not complaining 'bout that; for after all is said and done, they did me a good favour because it is only after that that I made up me mind to leave Trinidad and do something with my, my . . ." Phoebe's voice faltered. A sob rose like a bubble from some deep, troubled spring, interrupted the rhythm of her breathing. She dug out again her crumpled, flimsy handkerchief to dab at the tears now brimming over into streams down her cheeks. Thelma was trying to stop her own sympathetic tears from flowing freely. She looked away, seeming to take an unusual interest in the blue-and-white chequered pattern of the tablecloth.

"I know, Phoebe, I do understand. You haven't had it easy since you come to England, with not finding work and all the other problems finding somewhere to live. I know; that's how it is at first until you get used to it."

Phoebe looked quite exhausted. She sat clutching a shrunken ball of a sodden handkerchief and started staring through the people at the next table, and beyond the café wall as if it were transparent.

"I believe," ventured Thelma, "that the reason why you getting these bad dreams is because deep down you unhappy."

This remark seemed to pull Phoebe back into the present. She turned to look at Thelma. She said nothing, but the look in her wet eyes appeared to acknowledge some good sense in what her friend said.

I think we better go home." She said after a short while.

"Then you not going to the pictures?"

"No. I don't feel like it."

"Oh, come on Phoebe, it'll do you good. You just going to go home and brood if you don't come."

"No, tonight I going to look at the telly and maybe write a letter to Ma."
With this last remark, Phoebe left the table like someone who had suddenly
remembered something very important that should have been done some
time ago. Thelma hurried after her.

Hours later, Phoebe was sitting disconsolately in her sparsely furnished
bedsit. It was a room in an old, ramshackle, three-storey house in Lewisham.
Sounds of life echoed through the house: the uncertain notes of an alto
saxophone attempting to play the St Louis Blues was coming from the room
directly above her own; across the corridor a baby was crying its little heart
out whilst the high-pitched, admonishing voice of its exasperated mother
ran like a contrapuntal melody in some avant-garde musical experiment;
knuckles were being rapped impatiently on the door of the room next to
hers; from a television set, somewhere in the building, the sound of gunshots
followed by the diminishing whine of ricocheting bullets could be heard.

All these noises seemed to push Phoebe deeper into her own depressive
silence. Her thoughts wandered aimlessly over the scenes of her first
experiences in the 'mother country'. She saw herself standing in Victoria
railway station, shocked by the cold, in spite of the heavy overcoat she was
advised to wear - and it was only October and not winter yet. But what had
been even more shocking was the constantly shifting sea of grey faces set in
an expression of cold, startled curiosity. Where was the pink, healthy
complexion of the English in England? She remembered when she worked as
a servant for the Millses she used to dust and admire an old tinted
photograph of Queen Victoria which hung over the false mantlepiece of
their tropical bungalow. She also remembered her book, 'Little Women' with
illustrations of English girls with lovely pink complexions.

Where were the smiles of welcome? The only happy faces had belonged
to the West Indians who had come to meet relatives and friends. The
memory of how startling black by contrast these faces had been amidst the
cold, grey faces of the English, was still very sharp. Thelma had been
amongst them, but not even her bright infectious grin could have dispelled
completely the discomforting shadow which had hung over them on that
October day in Victoria railway station. She remembered how, for the first
time, she had been overwhelmed by the strange new awareness of her colour.

Her glimpse of London from the taxi had been very interesting. London
had looked tall and very crowded. She had found the streets curiously
narrow. What had taken her by surprise had been the awelessness of the
English people as they went about their daily affairs. For her it had been an
astonishing sight to see white beggars on the street corners.

The wailing siren of a police car crashed through her thoughts and
drowned completely all the various noises in the house. As it faded away as
suddenly as it had come, the noisesome bustle of the other flats and bedsits
in the old Victorian house resumed their usual level of decibels.

Phoebe's mood seemed altered. She remembered the letter she wanted
to write to her Ma. She found writing paper in her suitcase under the bed and
sat down at a little table, whose battered, burnt and grease-stained surface
testified to its multi-purpose usage. She cleared an area of the surface and,
biting the top of her biro, stared at the wall in search of inspiration.

After a few minutes she began writing: 'Dear Ma, I hope this letter finds you hale and hearty and that you bad leg don't hurt as much.' Phoebe resumed chewing the top of her biro. She debated with herself whether to write about her unhappiness and relate her dreams to her moth-er. She decided not to because her mother, in spite of being a tough and determined old lady, still worried about her, the last child and only daughter, even though she was twenty-seven years old. And she did not want to be the one to destroy the myth nurtured by people back home that England was some sort of magic place where West Indians became rich very fast.

'Well, things here,' she continued to write, 'is fine. At the moment I putting aside a little money to pay a deposit on a nice little house, so I can't send you anything for a little while.' Phoebe felt a lump come into her throat and lodge itself painfully there. She was not used to lying to her mother, but she believed it had to be done. Her mother must never know how hard it was for her to find work. She must never know that she was living in a dingy bedsit with hardly any furniture, and that having used up all the savings she had brought to England, owed rent to Ethel her Jamaican landlady.

'How is my little ground provision garden at the back of the house. I hope you looking after it. I did love that little garden. It was my pride and joy. If you find it too much work ask Horace, Ma Cumberbatch little granson, to help you when he come back from school. He is a nice little boy. Have you seen any of my worthless brothers recently? You know, they should be looking after you in your old age instead of playing the big-shot and gallivanting all over the Caribbean. Well, Ma, I sure glad I have my old school-friend Thelma over here with me. She is a real God-send. She make me very, very happy. I want you to look after yourself, Ma, and don't worry about me. Till the next time. Your loving daughter, Phoebe.

Phoebe folded the letter very thoughtfully, put it into an envelope which she addressed and laid aside for posting. Days later Phoebe was sitting in Fellini's Café waiting for Thelma. This time she did not have to wait long, a mere fifteen minutes. Thelma came into the café wearing her inimitable grin.

"Hi Phoebe, girl, what you doing!"

"So-so, Thelma."

"You stop dreaming, eh?"

A shadow of emotions passed over Phoebe's face.

"Well, as you come to mention it, no."

"Gord, Phoebe, when is it going to end?"

"Don't know, just so damn fed up with it all."

"Let me go and get some hot chocolate; tell me when I get back."

Thelma placed her handbag on the table and bounced up to the counter ordering two cups of hot chocolate on her way. Enrico Fellini's grin was so wide, it seemed audible above the noise of the Expresso coffee he was churning up for a pimply punk youth, who did not know what to make of Thelma. After her usual repartee with Enrico, she returned to the table with the hot chocolate and apple pie. "You never learn, Thelma. One day that man go get really fresh with you."

Thelma did not respond to this remark. She just grinned.

"Well then," she said, "let we hear this dream."

"It is not as frightening as the last one, but believe me Thelma, it is weird. Really, really weird."

Phoebe bit her lips and shook her head from side to side to register the improbable nature of the events in her dream.

"Come on, Phoebe, let we hear this dream." Thelma was leaning forward on the table, eyes shining.

"Right. I was in Port-of-Spain walking 'round the Queens Park Savannah. I was dressed all in white. The sun was shining kind of silvery, like one of them days when the wind cool and the sky blue with a whole heap of clouds like cotton wool floating."

"Eh-eh, Phoebe, you is a poet!"

"I telling you, it was exactly like that. I can see it all now, as clear as daylight."

Phoebe bit into her apple pie and slurped her hot chocolate. Thelma eyed her impatiently.

"I was walking along when suddenly I find myself in church with sun streaming through the stained glass window in all sorts of pretty colours. My young brother, Eric, was getting married. And guess who he was getting married to; he was getting married to you."

At this, Thelma laughed her high-pitched laugh. Several customers in the cafe turned to look at her with discreet smiles of amusement on their faces. Phoebe lowered her voice with embarrassment as she continued to relate her dream:

"A whole lot of people was in the wedding. There was Ethel, my Jamaican landlady; Mr Mills, my old boss back home; his floozie wife, still with her baggy dress, dirty plimsolls and blond hair all over the place; all my other brothers was there too, and my Ma and most of the people in the house where I am staying now. There was even people I never seen in my life. Suddenly there was a black cat at my feet. He was curling he tail around my legs. You bend down and pick 'im up. I don't know how it happen, but the black cat in your arms turn into a white baby. It was laughing and you was tickling it under the chin. Then at that point we was no longer in the church but in a big, big greenhouse with plenty, plenty plants and palm trees. We was having a wedding reception. Everybody was having a hell-of-a-time, dancing and eating. I was dancing with Enrico Fellini and Mr Mills was standing in his khaki short pants and white cork hat under one of the palm trees looking blue murder. I think he was vex and jealous because of me dancing with Enrico. Then the scene change again and I was lying in me bed. Mervin, me old boyfriend, was bending over me and giving me a kiss-an-a-half. His tongue was all down me throat. I couldn't breathe. I wake up all of a sudden to find the blanket covering me face. I must admit, I was disappointed it was only a dream."

"Phoebe, that is what I call one hell-of-a erotic dream."

"Listen, I know an erotic dream when I have one, and that wasn't one of them."

"I was just teasing. Is really an interesting dream. Have you never try to interpret your dreams?"

"Not really. I hear some people say that you dream when you go to bed with food resting on your stomach."

"That's stupid talk, Phoebe. Dreams, they dead important. I read somewhere is your unconscious talking to you."

"Me what?"

"Your unconscious trying to tell you something."

"Well, you learn something new every day. I know sometimes when I unhappy I get bad dreams, like the time Mervin left me for that Cocorite jamette."

"I tell you something, Phoebe, maybe we should try to interpret your dreams."

Thelma's happy, mobile face showed a rare moment of seriousness. Phoebe sat in a quiet tension of expectancy, eyes fixed on her friend's grave expression.

"I think Jumbie had something to do with your dreams."

Phoebe looked aghast.

"Wherever there is a black dog, black cat, black bird or black anything, you bet your life Jumbie have something to do with it."

"I don't see exactly what you mean," Phoebe countered, "Jumbie only work they business in Trinidad, not here in England."

"Girl, you must be joking! Look, them Jumbies have no bounds. Time and space mean nothing to them. They could meddle in your affairs here in England just as easily as they do in Trinidad. Anyway, your black dog, Toby, in your dreams is really a Jumbie."

"But I thought you say is my unconscious that is trying to tell me something."

"Well yes, your unconscious comes sometimes as a Jumbie."

"Okay then, what he come to tell me 'bout?"

"About England, what else! You know how you catching your arse here: no job; and you almost didn't have somewhere to lay your head at night if I didn't go an plead with Ethel to let you have the room you in now. Answer me this: why you think you have all the problems?"

A trapped look came over Phoebe's face. "I don't really know," she answered, "I suppose because things in England hard."

"I suppose because things in England hard," mimicked Thelma, rolling her eyes in disbelief. "Well, I have news for you, girl: things ain't hard, it's bloody diabolical. It's prejudice; stark raw, racial prejudice. That Jumbie come to tell you to watch your step."

Phoebe quietly considered this for a second or two, then asked, "What about the ground bleeding?"

"I don't know about that. I guess it could mean suffering or something."

"It remind me of something I once heard on television in one of them programmes about Black people. There was a black poet talking 'bout the blood of slaves spilled for freedom in the soil of the West Indies. You think the bleeding ground in my dream had something to do with the dead slaves in our history?" Phoebe looked away. She appeared a little embarrassed.

"Between you and me, Thelma," she said confidentially, "there's something that happen a long time ago when I was still working for Mr Mills.

I never told anybody before. All these years I keep it to myself."

Thelma could not disguise her eager curiosity.

"Well, let's have it."

"When I used to work for Mr Mills, on Tuesdays I clean up the bungalow and wash the dirty clothes. Mrs Mills who hated any kind of work - even seeing other people do it - always visited she friend, Mrs Blanc, on the days I in the house cleaning. I didn't mind because then I had the house to meself an I could work in peace. One Tuesday while I was in the bedroom making the beds, I hear a noise as though somebody come in the house. Girl, I nearly wet my pants with fright. Then the bedroom door open and Mr Mills standing there covered from head to foot in stinking black mud. I think he must have fall down somewhere on his cocoa estate. He didn't say a word. He just grap a towel and head for the shower. I started to hurry up making the beds so that I could finish early and get out of the house; but after two minutes Mr Mills was standing in the doorway again naked as the day he was born. I telling you Thelma, from the looks of him he was ready to do business. Well I scream out really loud. He rushed up and put his hand over me mouth and he hold me tight, tight. I tried to struggle away but it was though I was in a vice. I could feel his hot breath all over me face as he was telling me how he always liked me, how when Ida - that is Mrs Mills' name - is lying in bed besides him at night snoring, he is wide awake thinking about me and wondering how it would be like doing it with me; that I must keep it a secret between me and he, and if I didn't I shall have to find another job . . ."

"The bastard. You should have raised you knee hard in he crotch."

"He was so strong, I didn't have a chance. Well, no need to go into the details; you can guess what happen."

The corners of Phoebe's mouth quivered as she fought to hold back her tears. "I can see now," Thelma said, "why he appear so often in your dreams. An experience like that is bound to mark you for life. I know for sure now that your dreams is all about your problems here; and maybe it is not just your problem. Your Jumbie is telling you that just as that old devil boss of yours raped you, so did all them white colonial people. They take advantage of us and leave us no better off. And it still happening."

"What 'bout Mr Arundel; how he fit into me dream?"

"That Englishman teacher! As far as I can remember, he had two passions: history of his beloved England and a bottle of rum. It was he who put them ideas in you head about England being the great mother country, and ruling the waves and all that nonsense, especially when he was drunk."

"And me last dream, what you think about that one?"

"Ah well, that dream is different - more hopeful. Things going to change for you, mark my words, Phoebe. Just keep listening to your Jumbie."

Phoebe's face was a sky of shifting grey clouds letting some sunlight through. This session of trying to interpret her bad dreams appeared to have had a therapeutic effect on her.

"Come on, Thelma, let's go to the cinema. What's on?"

"I think a love story called 'The Other Woman', or something like that."

"Sounds good." The two friends linked arms and left Fellini's café in a lighter mood.

Phoebe was up early the next day with a new determination to find work. In the past she had scoured the classified ads in most of the newspapers and had found clerical positions for which she had applied. She had had several interviews along with other hopefuls, most of them white. It had not taken her long to become thoroughly disheartened with her lack of success. Thelma had advised her to forget the way people thought back home in Trinidad about the white collar job being a 'decent', worthwhile ambition; that here in England, as a Black person, it really did not matter what job you did as long as you could survive with some dignity; and that she should start looking for any job: cleaning floors, washing up in restaurants, anything.

In her new mood, Phoebe at last decided to take Thelma's advice. She found the courage to do something which she, in moments of desperate frustration, had always thought of doing. She selected a main street in the city with many shops and businesses; then systematically entered every door to ask for work. In some shops with their awe-inspiringly sleek and stylish interiors, she raised a snigger by the mere incongruity of her physical presence. In others her enquiries were met with raised eyebrows of astonishment and the silence of being caught off guard; sometimes even arrogance of the Olympian kind she had often seen parodied in some of the dated films she had seen in Trinidad. Phoebe took it all, but there were moments when she came very close to giving up.

The main street seemed never to end. She grew very tired. Since eight o'clock in the morning she had been looking for work. Her stomach was telling her it was time for lunch. As she turned to enter a fish and chips bar, an old beggar came up to her, extended his gnarled, arthritic fingers and begged with his eyes. They were strange, soft eyes whose eloquent pleading went straight to her heart. This beggar carried with him the aroma of rum like an aura. His thin, wiry, bare arms and scrubbing-board chest gave the impression of his being pickled and cured like dried meat.

As Phoebe handed the beggar a coin, the strange familiarity of his wry smile stirred vague, shapeless memories. He shuffled away muttering to himself. She entered the fish bar, her heart pounding. There is something about that beggar's eyes and wry smile that troubled her.

Next to her at the counter were noisy youths with strange haircuts and black leather jackets emblazoned with chauvinistic statements. Each jacket vied with the other for the most ornately colourful version of 'NF'. Phoebe felt anxious and vulnerable in such close proximity with them.

One of their group, a dangly, scraggily-haired youth had painted 'THERE'LL ALWAYS BE AN ENGLAND' under his 'NF'. This statement leapt out at Phoebe and reminded her of the image of Mr Arundel in her dream. It was then that she realised with a sudden and indescribable alarm that the old beggar was Mr Arundel, her Englishman teacher, who taught her history many years ago in Trinidad.

Her mind was in turmoil. What ill fortune had occurred to reduce Mr Arundel to this sorry state? She remembered him in Trinidad; how dignified he looked and spoke, even in his bouts of drunkenness. He had represented for her then the image of a charming, educated, though eccentric breed of

Illustration by John Lyons

Englishman; not at all like that tanned, weather-beaten old pirate, Mr Mills.

Phoebe felt curiously let down. Her ideas about England and the English were suddenly in even greater disarray than on the day she had arrived. As she retraced her steps to her bedsit she was filled with ambivalent feelings of unease and an indeterminate sense of being on the brink of some momentous discovery. It was that odd feeling as if a diaphanous membrane separated her from the great meaning of life.

She remembered when Mr Arundel was leaving the school in Tunapuna, many years ago. He made a speech about regretfully having to leave Trinidad and its beautiful people, but that there was no other place like his great country, England, and that he was overjoyed to be able to return home to a retirement of leisure.

Phoebe remembered his passion for rum and wondered if it was that had cor-rupted his self-reliance and energetic lust for life. She imagined him spending all his money in endless supplies of nothing but the best rum. An overwhelming sympathy swept over her like a tidal wave; but in an odd way, it was a sympathy from which she could feel herself drawing strength.

In the days which followed, Phoebe did a great deal of thinking. She also continued to search for work. In spite of her new strength and positive outlook, she remained unsuccessful. However, she did not feel the same about being told 'no'. She shrugged her shoulders and muttered under her breath, 'your loss', and carried on.

Phoebe, much to her own surprise, found herself thinking about a new hair style: 'Why not?' she thought, 'I feel different, so I go look different; anyway, I can't wait to see the look on Thelma's face when she clap eyes on the new Phoebe'. Having made her decision, she wasted no time in asking Edna Rivers in the top floor bedsit to plait her hair in the African style she had always admired on other Black women. Edna, who was an 'easy-go-lucky' type of young woman, was flattered that Phoebe should ask her. She wanted to start right away. Three hours later Phoebe emerged a different woman. She was looking forward with great excitement to meeting Thelma.

Thelma was standing at the counter in Fellini's Cafe. She was agitated. "Enrico, did you see my frien come in here?"

"No, sweetheart." Enrico's lascivious grin did not get the usual response.

"This is serious, Enrico. something must have happen to her. She never, never late; is me who always late, not she."

Just at that point Phoebe walked into the cafe. Thelma looked as though she saw a creature from another planet.

"Sorry I late, Thelma." Phoebe was enjoying the look of astonishment on her friend's face.

"Is it really you, Phoebe! What happen? Girl, you look fabulous in you new hairstyle." She turned to Enrico. "Enrico, you better look out." Enrico, his mouth open in surprise, was spilling milk all over the counter.

"Thelma," Phoebe said with uncharacteristic bravado, "today we drinking Expresso coffee, but you still paying."

"You really, really look great, Phoebe."

"Listen Thelma, another one of those 'you really, really look great' and I go feel insulted."

"What bring on this change of personality, then?"

"I waking up, Thelma, I just waking up."

"What happen, you meet that good kisser you been dreaming about?"

"Nothing like that. And something else, I stop dreaming. Anyway, I got lots to tell you."

"And so have I, but that can wait. Let's hear what you been up to first."

"I was window-shopping, that is why I late."

"You been WHAT?"

"Window-shopping."

"Hey, you come into some money, or what?"

"No, but . . ."

"Then you find a job?"

"No. Listen Thelma, I just been doing a lot of thinking and I feel different. That's all."

Thelma still did not look convinced. Her eyes quizzically searched the face of her friend.

"You remember my last dream, Thelma. Remember you tell me that things going to change for me? Well, you right. I don't understand how it happen, but I definitely began to feel different after I saw Mr Arundel."

"Hold on, Phoebe, I thought I hear you say you stop dreaming."

"I don't mean I see 'im in my dream. I really saw 'im."

"Phoebe, you not making sense. Explain."

"Well, I was out looking for work, when just as I was going into a fish and chip bar, this old beggar comes up to me begging. He didn't say anyting; he just look at me in a way which make me feel funny. I didn't have much money on me, but there was no way I could refuse 'im. There was something vaguely familiar about the way he smile. It was a bit like deja vu. Is only when I went into the fish and chip place and I see painted on a leather jacket, 'There'll always be an England' that it all come back suddenly to me. I knew then that the old beggar was Mr Arundel. He was old and mash-up, very skinny. Odd though, the only thing that remain fresh is that peculiar smile of his and those soft, soft eyes. Oh yes, the other thing, he stinking of rum."

"You sure you not mistaken, Phoebe? This is one hell-of-a thing to happen, mind-blowing."

"Honest to Gord, Thelma; every word I tell you is gospel."

"Did you run after him?"

"No, I was so shocked I didn't know what to do; and when I leave the fish and chip bar, he already gone. He disappear as if it was really a dream. But I know it was no dream. He was standing there as plain as the nose on your face." Thelma was shaking her head from side to side in an expression of incredulity.

"Jumbie working he thing really, really good. Jumbie talk to you in your dreams, now he working magic in broad daylight."

"I telling you, Thelma, I went straight home after that, me thoughts like bacchanale in me head. That night I didn't sleep, so I didn't dream. I don't know when I doze off, but I got up next morning with an unusually clear head feeling good and ready to face the world, looking for work."

Despite Thelma's genuine interest in Phoebe's adventures, it was also becoming more and more evident from her growing agitation, that what she had to tell Phoebe was straining at the doors of her lips to be let out.

"Phoebe, I got to tell you. I met this guy called Thomasin at me cousin last weekend. He very nice-looking, but he not the rugged type I go for. However, he invite me to have drinks at his place in Brockley Rise."

"Well, that's great news, Thelma. You luck changing."

"Don't talk wet, Phoebe. Anyway I tell him I come only if I could bring me best friend with me."

"Why you want to do a thing like that?"

"Safety in numbers, Phoebe," she said with a wink.

"I don't have anything to wear."

"Come on, stop making stupid excuses. We only going for drinks for heaven sake. Anyway, you know you can always borrow one of my dresses if you want to."

"Okay I'll come, but only just this once."

As Thelma left Phoebe that Friday evening, she chuckled to herself and muttered under her breath, 'this time, my girl, I think I found the answer to all your problems. No more dreaming, no more looking for work and living in that stinking hole your landlady call a bedsit. I sure you go like him and he go like you.'

The next day, Saturday afternoon, Phoebe is sitting in the unfamiliar sitting-room of Thomasin's flat in a trance of admiration. Her eyes, which shone with a glazed brilliance, were fixed on the handsome face of her host as she hung on his every word. Something had already stirred within her when she saw his garden. She had never seen such a healthy green garden outside of her native Trinidad. It was a spot of green in the depressive grey of London's atmosphere. He had coaxed into luxuriant growth spinach, potatoes, tomatoes, sweetcorn, runner beans and a variety of aromatic herbs. Phoebe remembered her own garden in Tunapuna and felt nostalgia and a flood of affection which was already flowing towards Thomsain.

For Phoebe, Thelma might as well have not been there. All life was focused on the microcosm of that space with Phoebe and Thomasin. Everything and everybody else were excluded. Quietly she was reaching the point of ecstasy as he talked about his garden of the future, creating a home away from his Jamaican home. He showed her his plans for a greenhouse covering the entire space of his back yard. He had designed on paper special temperature controls to permit the growth of yams, sweet potatoes, cassava and other vegetables of a tropical garden. The warmth that circled around Phoebe's heart moved downwards awakening feelings she once had for another a long time ago in Trinidad. She sat searching her dreams for a greenhouse in Brockley Rise.

John Lyons

?

Saqi Farooqi

MASTANA HEEJRA

God,
It was frost-cold
That is why
Mastana, the eunuch
Whiskeyed up
Before he came onto the street . . .

Tennis balls trapped
In a taut tight bra
Became his bulging breasts.
Rivulets of lust
In red streaks
Played in mascaraed eyes . . .

Walking in gay abandon
He swivelled his hips
Again and again
Inviting
The roguish punters-in-heat.
His boisterous bum
Filling their desolate hearts
With a strange seductive beat . . .

He rubbed the meaty mounds
Of hennaed palms, then clapped
Releasing butterflies of colour
Into the fragrant air.
His fleshy, sensual lips
(Full of pan-blood kisses)
Rang like dancing bells
And bubbled,
Burst in excitement
Raining nectar into mother-pearls
Of wandering eyes . . .

He was in great form
Like a debutante
Enticing and alluring.
His nostrils swelling
And fingers dancing
In flagrant wild
Ecstatic gestures . . .

Suddenly he stopped
And laughed and said:
"You lucky bastards

I have been
Drowning in tears
Helplessly
Since time began
And lie buried alive
In this narrow tomb . . .
. . . this death-trap of
World's bloody conscience." (Trs: Mahmood Jamal)

THE LIE

Words
    beheading
        words.

But in that hush . . .
. . . That furious gush of silence
Her maiden speech
Drowned.
She went with it.

During the postmortem
When the knives were out
Carving - n - flensing
The stillborn
Deliberations

The lie was found
Buried in fact
Near cul-de-sac-subconscious
Right across the electric field
Of her magnetic self.

Alive
    indispensable
        intact.

A POEM CALLED KILDARE

Kildare is not there
Damn it -
Where is Kildare?

- Don't know who -
But somebody said
That he only existed
Between a suffocating silence
And a violent burst of tears
(which is true)
Hence - his disappearance.

My disapproving dog,
Christened Mr Comrade,
Followed his lurking scent
Then let him go.
(I think it was him in the park
Couldn't be too sure -
- Was a kind of hazy-dark,
A dim state of doubt)
He took a crooked corner
And went out.

When I saw him last - he was
Desperate, really desperate
Munching his libido
Lying in wait
Licking his memory-wounds
Grinding his jaws.

He swallowed his ego
Smelt of bad breath
Was finally consumed by stress
While flirting with loneliness
Sinking in life-marsh and
Forming a liaison with death.

Kildare is not there
Damn it -
Where is Kildare?

Saqi Farooqi

Shaheed Quaderi

THE EYES OF FRIENDS

Under the eagle-eyed gaze of friends
I bumble through the hot bazaar,
My bright black eyes suspended in theirs
Like stale beef in a sunlit stall;
Like a slab of stale meat I lie
Inside the eyes behind the eagle-eyed gaze of friends,
Eye to eye I'm a glistening chunk of meat in sunlight
Amidst drone of filthy flies, buzz of friends' eyes,
Hanging in eyes of friends, hanging from their beaks,
Swinging in the breeze, a hunk of discoloured meat
Gaily dangling in the fetid breath of friends. O look
At my blue veins and arteries -
                              waving streamers!
My best friend's eyes

Mounted on a table on a pair of strong legs,
Unblinking,
Ticking away with my heartbeats,
Pounding in my brain, in the pulse on my wrist,
My best friend's eyes
Ring
Ding-dong all around me
And follow me restlessly
As I sit down, stand up, walk, turn about,
Or simply stand
                    alone
              on the dark verandah
My best friend's eyes
Ring
From the clock-tower
With a loud ding-dong
Telling everyone
I'm finished

AT EACH OTHER

We stare at each other
in this dark.

The owl's piercing screech
marks an endless scratch
on the body of night.

Torn fragmentary images emerge
from some dark secret source;
a drunken stallion rears
up through air into the void;
read as a chinarose the moon hangs in the garden.

Your day abruptly becomes a rainbow
and I like a crab
in sterile revelry can only make
one wound after another.

Suddenly these wounds
raise their eager absorbed faces at me
like a drunkard's flaming eyes.

Our entwined limbs draw us closer.
Yet, drowning the weird, absurd feelings
these scenes evoke,
your tears can't touch me.

Trans: Kaiser Haq

Rafiq Azad

ART AND HUNGER

My dog: back from solitary investigations:
'Lord, mankind doesn't really
care for flowers; they love the smell
of bread and vegetables much more. Still,
raising doleful invocations -
O Rose! My Rose! - is their habit.
This was explained to me
in an hour-long spiel
by a woman lovely as a rose.'

LOVE

A blind woman
standing
in front of a massive door
locked tight & heavy
as mercury -

wrong key in hand   Trans: Kaiser Haq

Kaiser Haq

SLIPPERS

Distant thunder turns into the alarm
ringing. Eyes open and shut
open and shut, each time making
new shapes, new colours.
Green hills and pink clouds on sheets.
Brown arms sprout from shoulders,
knotty fingers from hands. They lift
the blue mosquito net. At once
a pair of legs complete with feet, toes
swings through, lands on the floor.
Eyes follow but land on slippers
instead, and stay there. Poets
given to fancy might compare them
to the arms of a bride waiting for the groom,
to twin-ponies of a chariot,
to wings ready to take off.
I feel a shiver; it isn't the cold floor:
they're worn so thin, my old rubber flip-flops.

from **Evening Star**

Dea Trier Mørch

Then a picture of Simon's great idol joins the others on the bonfire - the great Soviet poet Mayakovsky - against a background of scraps depicting ships and flowers.

Simon throws another idol onto the flames. A Jesus face with a black beret on. Che Guevara. Down in one corner, Simon has copied one of Picasso's harlequin figures.

The flames eat through the canvas, curling it up. The back frame breaks with a crack.

"I'm burning that," Simon cries, "because it represents the illusions of '68."

"You're burning them to punish yourself," mumbles Niels Peter, now almost as drunk as his brother.

"In future, I'm only going to do pictures on paper," says Simon. "Paper burns better."

Niels Peter thumps him on the shoulder.

"Mind you don't burn the whole house down."

"Shall we . . . ?" says Simon, drawing back his lips so that his silver front tooth catches the firelight. "Shall we get a can of petrol?"

He throws his arm back and flings the empty bottle into the night.

She was clinging on to life on the earth's surface. He knew it. She couldn't let go . . .

He disentangled himself from his bedclothes and stood at his mother's bedhead. It was seven in the morning on the last day.

"Did you manage to sleep?"

"Yes," she whispered, with tears in her eyes and trembling lips.

Perhaps she simply hadn't slept at all.

"Would you like a little water?"

She blinked.

That meant yes.

"How are we?" said the morning nurse as she gently and calmly prepared her patient for the day of her death. "A home-help is coming tomorrow or the day after."

The nurse and Niels Peter tried to get Bett into a shirt, one that Isia had bought for him in Italy. Bett had wanted it herself, because it was so soft. A few weeks earlier, she had asked Niels Peter if he would cut the collar and sleeves off, because they were uncomfortable.

It looked so disfigured.

He tried to get her arm through the armhole.

Her face contorted.

"Niels Peter," she whispered. "You're breaking my arm."

He almost wept. He kissed her hand - and the stubble on his chin scraped it as he said:

"Forgive me. Forgive me for being so clumsy."

Bett's eyes were blank. When she spoke, she had difficulty forming the words:

"I feel . . . feel . . . so strange. So listless . . ."

"Yes?"

"Are you giving me . . . some medicine . . . I don't know about?"

He showed her the jars of pills.

"It's only the Doloxene and the Kerogen - you know about them."

The morning nurse nodded in confirmation and packed her bag.

Bett looked dubiously at her son.

He felt as if his hair was turning white. As white as hers.

"Goodbye," said the nurse, and emerged onto the hot, suffocating streets of Copenhagen.

"Take my hand," she said all of a sudden.

Her hand was astonishingly cold, the nails ribbed and as white as paper. They both stared up at the ceiling. Thus they were united for a minute or two.

Then he did something that he knew immediately he would think about a great many times later in life. And regret.

"I'm just going to . . ."

He let go of her hand and went into the kitchen, where he added:

". . . turn off the coffee."

He turned off the coffee-maker, poured himself a cup, added some milk and lit a cigarette.

She said "take my hand", he thought. Now she's gliding into the very last stage. I can feel it in the very molecules of her body. What wouldn't I have given earlier in my life, to be able to hold her hand in a situation like this? Why do I turn away now? I took her hand. Then I let it go. Instead of holding on as long as was necessary . . .

He went back in and took his mother's hand again.

but now it no longer mattered.

There, the search was over.

Folded the camp-bed and placed it against the wall. Emptied the dishwasher. Ran up and down the stairs with various things in his hands.

Niels Peter's intention had been ot create perfect calm. But instead he rushed about frantically, his thoughts flitting about . . . clothers, washing, pills, time, letters, finances, the family.

There was a knock at the door. Outside was Lajla. Radiant, her arms bare and sun-tanned.

"How are things?" she said breathlessly.

He jerked his head.

"Bett's having her midday sleep. It'll soon be over."

"It was so important to me that she didn't die," whispered Lajla, "before I came back from my holiday. Can I help with anything?"

"Yes, with everything."

They stole in and looked through the door. Bett lay groaning in the high bed, her hands in a strange position on her stomach.

He tried to write a shopping list for Lajla. He needed some small plates. Simon's picture was to be framed. Two litres of apple juice. Some more stamps.

The letters looked all wrong.

He found it difficult to spell.

No cash.

Wrote a cheque.

Sent Lajla off.

Dea Trier Mørch

Marianne Larsen

THE MEADOW

this evening the meadow seems the essential thing
and because of it
what we talk about this evening
includes stalks and streams and frogs
and insects and eggs and blackbirds
and lack of worries about work contracts
this evening
not far from us children are walking
hand in hand with their grown-ups
it is a meadow
true, there's a city on top of it

(From *Statement to Follow*, 1978)

ORDINARY HUMAN ARMS

we put our arms around each other
a pair of ordinary tax-paying human arms
not to rest them
but to harden them
a pair of ordinary concrete-accustomed
and marketed human arms
a pair of ordinarily needing
a pair of ordinarily hugging
human arms
we put them around each other
they are health-insured and ordinarily dressed
a pair of ordinary love-interpreting
human arms

how strong they are
sovereign, independent -
no matter where
no matter what the hour
no matter what the season
suddenly and for all time
human arms
without speculation
we put them around each other
as if to show that their powerlessness
doesn't exist

(From *Who is the Enemy?*, 1977)

(untitled)

prisoners leaning against each other
neck inclined to neck
spread out over black squares

the treetops they can't see
seem crazy to them

they speak
with something they hit on
by themselves
to use as language and longing
in one

the difficult utterance
of their distant eyes
of their shadow coloured garments'
identical folds

the cramp they get
in legs and arms and throat to grow
in the midst of all that paralysis
from outermost to inmost

the difficult utterance
of their drawn breath
of all that's bound

they can't do it
and they do.

(From *Suddenly This*, 1985)
Trans: Anne Born

Patrick Clark

LAZARUS

And you brought me back for this?
From the stinginess of death?
How I wish you'd saved your breath.
Death was beatific bliss.

Final answer of the brain
to the question of the heart:
pia mater falls apart
end of pleasure, end of pain.

All nonentity the night,
no identity the dawn;
neither will nor way, nor wight;
evil's consciousness withdrawn.

Now I shuffle among friends,
back alive in a new bondage.
I still stink of the last bandage,
and such otherness offends.

Now, I wither into spring
where the drinkers at their task
snigger as my tragic mask
crumples into soundless song.

And you brought me back for this
from the nothingness of Sheol?
Woke my putrefying soul -
cracked ego, spent spark
extradited by the dark?

I belonged in the abyss.

MIRACULOUS

Weeding his earth, he trailed
from their incense-rich root-run a bine
of buttercups, cleavers, couch-grass,
self-seeking, entangled, dear green.

"The hem of his cloak" silence said,
recalling the woman who bled,

(how does light come in one's head?)
Whole through the touch of the twill
bobbing at the holy man's heel.

And silence dove-thundered and
spoke through the green in his hand,
echoing the ancient plea:
"May I be cured, Sir, of me?"

THE NIGHT THEY SOLD THE LOCAL

Now is the humming of the planet
drowned by the hubbub of the pub.
Now the mute menhirs,
miraculously vertical,
are legs to primeval ideas.

Each cerebrum posthistoric
misted with the ancient anger
reshapes the original trauma:
selfhood's ancient kingdom
taken over by the stranger,
lost like the other causes
in all the loss of history.

Keening minds we revolve
in the snoring of the planet unheard.

BELONGING

Horizontal snow-winds underline
how growth's mere slavery to the sacred sun.
Snowdrops assume their crucial role in time,
roused by rapt choirs of hydrogen and helium.

Snowflakes, in their hydrostatic mystery,
obey, like flowers, the dying laws of physics,
set, like the other molecules of history,
to temporal rhythms, to entropic music.

And you? Does consciousness that in your brain,
your blood, your skin corroborates these laws
hint, sometimes, that the I which hosts the pain
lives a dimension rarer than all those?

Comb your hair. See? Atoms fall from your crown.
Deafening like snow. Now. Strike the silence-gong.
Get to the root of things. Take the way down.
Admit it. Snow belongs. You don't belong.

MURDER POLIS

These two glistening corpses stiff with salt
are what I did last night.
Black silent screams contorting from assault
they scandalising the light.

Now thoughts of burial have my nerves in rags.
Am I d'you think, hell-bent?
Stowing the guts of two erotic slugs?

Ask me, go on, to repent.

THE UNBORN

Abba, in your blood I hear the music,
the atoms in helical choirs, the hymns of the holy
virus, islands wild with the sea-borne's perfume,
paraclete I her womb's illumination.

In your scented blood, Abba, light's epiphanies,
honey-fierce dawn fanfaring the glow-worm's majesty;
stars obsessed with their entangled orbits
latching their threads round the recoiling chromosomes.

Comes the first taste of the dark. No, says earth's goddess:
Do not presume your love or you are precious.
People so early flawed invite love's censure.

Dark tastes the mouth unborn. The serpent selfhood
preens unconsciousness in our conception's ecstasy.
Through umbilical glades doom's feminine odour
keens back to the original rank flowering.

Abba, I hear the sobbing in the sacred wood,
all our innocent atoms balefully betrayed.
I smell my shore of tears, the rat-feet hirpling
over my mouth. I call you. Light me to the womb.

Patrick Clark

Andrew Fletcher of Saltoun

Scotland & Europe

An Account of a Conversation concerning a Right Regulation
of Governments for the common Good of Mankind

'Account of a Conversation' is the last work which can certainly be ascribed to Fletcher. Written as a dialogue, it purports to be a record of a conversation which occurred at a chance meeting in London between Fletcher, the Earl of Cromarty and two English politicians, Sir Christopher Musgrave and Sir Edward Seymour. Evidence that the conversation took place has yet to be found; the art with which the dialogue is developed and the genre of dialogue suggest that Fletcher carefully shaped what he published. The participants were well chosen. Cromarty, a notoriously self-seeking Scots politician, was also an intelligent advocate of incorporating union. The two Englishmen were Tories, in contrasting styles - Musgrave a "Country Party" MP from the North West, Seymour a West Country MP long part of the Tory leadership: they had recently joined in opposition to Irish commercial interests, and were clearly prepared to treat the Scots in the same way. The extract is from the first (1732) edition of Fletcher's 'Political Works'; I have retained the original spelling and punctuation, but introduced paragraphs. John Robertson.

I did not foresee, said Sir Chr-, what use you would make of my complaint against the depravation of manners that reigns in this town, but acknowledge the consequwence you draw to be just; and that if we design to diminish the corruption, we must lessen the city.

What visions have we here, said Sir Edw-rd? destroy the greatest and most glorious city of the world to prosecute a whimsical project!

Sir, replied I, you have not heard what I have answered to Sir Chr-; and besides, do you not think the remoter parts of England injured by being obliged to have recourse to London for almost everything, and particularly for justice? Do you not think them wronged, in that almost all the treasure of England is yearly laid out in this place, and by that means the substance of the other parts exhausted, and their rents and revenues diminished?

This, said he, is of little importance to the nation, so long as they continue to rise in the counties that lie nearest to the capital.

I do not know that, replied I, but am of opinion, that if instead of one, we had twelve cities in these kingdoms possessed of equal advantages, so many centers of men, riches and power, would be much more advantageous than one. For this vast city is like the head of a ricketty child, which by drawing to itself the nourishment that should be distributed in due proportions to the rest of the languishing body, becomes so over-charged, that frenzy and death unavoidably ensue. And if the number of people and their riches would be far greater in twelve cities than now in one, which I think no man will dispute; and that these cities were situated in convenient distances from each other, the relief and advantages they would bring to every part of these kingdoms would be unspeakable. For example, if the people of Yorkshire or Devonshire were not obliged to go further than York or Exeter to obtain justice, and consequently had no occasion to spend money out of those counties, how soon should we see another face of things in both? how soon would they double and treble their present value? That London should draw the riches and government of the three kingdoms to the south-east corner of this island, is in some degree as unnatural, as for one city to possess the riches and government of the world. And, as I said before, that men ought to be dispersed over all countries in greater or lesser numbers according to the fertility of the soil; so no doubt justice should be administered to all in the most convenient manner that may be, and no man obliged to seek it at an inconvenient distance. And if the other parts of government are not also communicated to every considerable body of men; but that some of them must be forced to depend upon others, and be governed by those who reside far from them, and little value any interest except their own, studying rather how to weaken them in order to make sure of their subjection; I say, all such governments are violent, unjust and unnatural.

I shall add, that so many different seats of government will highly encourage virtue. For all the same offices that belong to a great kingdom, must be in each of them; with this difference, that the offices of such a kingdom being always burdened with more business than any one man can rightly execute, most things are abandoned to the rapacity of servants; and the extravagant profits of all great officers plunge them into all manner of luxury, and debauch them from doing good: whereas the offices of these lesser governments extending only over a moderate number of people, will be duly executed, and many men have occasions put into their hands of doing good to their fellow citizens. So many different seats of government will highly tend to the improvement of all arts and sciences; and afford great variety of entertainment to all foreigners and others of a curious and inquisitive genius, as the ancient cities of Greece did.

I perceive now, said Sir Edw-rd, the tendency of all this discourse. On my conscience he has contrived the whole scheme to no other end than to set his own country on an equal foot with England and the rest of the world.

To tell you the truth, said I; the insuperable difficulty I found of making my country happy by any other way, led me insensibly to the discovery of these things; which, if I mistake not, have no other tendency than to render, not only my own country, but all mankind as happy as the imperfections of human nature will admit. For I considered that in a state of separation from England, my country would be perpetually involved in bloody and destructive wars. And if we should be united to that kingdom in any other manner, we must of necessity fall under the miserable and languishing condition of all places that depend upon a remote seat of government. And pray where lies the prejudice, if the three kingdoms were united on so equal a foot, as for ever to take away all suspicion and jealousy of separation? that virtue and industry might be universally incouraged, and every part contribute chearfully and in due proportion to the security and defence of this union, which will preserve us so effectually from those two great calamities, war and corruption of manners. This is the only just and rational kind of union. All other coalitions are but the unjust subjection of one people to another. Here I stopped; . . .

Andrew Fletcher of Saltoun

The Political Intelligence of Andrew Fletcher of Saltoun

John Robertson

The reputations of famous Scots tend to die hard: but the reputations of Andrew Fletcher of Saltoun (1653-1716) have died harder than most. In one popular view he is simply "The Patriot", the incorruptible, unreconciled foe of the 1707 Treaty of Union, who died praying to God to have mercy on "my poor Country that is so barbarously oppressed." In another, opposite but equally simple view, he is the eccentric enthusiast for the ancient world whose solution to the problem of poverty in late seventeenth-century Scotland was the enslavement of the entire labouring population. Each of these reputations has its origins in the opinions of his contemporaries, some of whom hailed him as "the Cato of our times", while others mocked his rigid principles; and both reputations were firmly established by the early nineteenth century. In the 1790s Fletcher the Patriot was honoured as a torch-bearer for the rights of man, his portrait topped by a cap of liberty; in 1840 the Glasgow *Chartist Circular* praised him as one who had nobly contended for "genuine political liberty". But Macaulay redressed the balance only eight years later, remarking sharply that Fletcher had so disdained the common people, and was so little disposed to entrust them with political power, that he thought them unfit to enjoy even personal freedom.

Since then Fletcher's twin reputations have endured virtually unchanged in the public consciousness. Two sober biographies, the first by G.W.T. Omond in the *Famous Scots* series (1897), and the second, a life and times by W.C. Mackenzie (1935), did not dispute the traditional images of the man; and a more recent republication of a selection of his writings by David Daiches (1979) offered no new assessment of his thought. (More seriously, perhaps, Daiches also neglected the opportunity to resolve outstanding bibliographical and textual questions about Fletcher's works.)

Nevertheless, the last twenty years have seen a remarkable growth of scholarly interest in Fletcher, and in particular in his political writings. These have been set by historians in two specific historical contexts. The first is the republican or "civic humanist" tradition of political thought, whose roots lay in classical antiquity, and which was rediscovered in the Italian Renaissance. Best restated by Machiavelli in his *Discourses on Livy*, this vein of republican theory passed into English political thought in the mid-seventeenth century, and thence eventually to America, where it inspired the demands of the colonists in 1776. The story of this passage of republican ideas from the Italian to the English-speaking worlds was brilliantly reconstructed by the New Zealand-born historian J.G.A. Pocock in a major book published in 1975; and in it Pocock accorded a significant place to Andrew Fletcher as one of a group of political writers at the turn of the seventeenth and eighteenth centuries who adapted the republican tradition to the conditions of an increasingly commercial society. In particular Pocock drew attention to Fletcher's sweeping historical analysis of the rise of standing armies in his *Discourses of Government with relation to Militias* (1698), where the emergence of the professional soldier was linked to the end of feudalism and the growth of princely power based on royal control of revenue and credit.

The mid-1970s also saw the Edinburgh historian Nicholas Phillipson begin a series of path-breaking studies of the origins and development of the Scottish Enlightenment, studies in which Fletcher has been a constant point of reference. Applied to the problems of Scotland, Phillipson has suggested, Fletcher's civic humanist principles produced a remarkably penetrating analysis of the nation's predicament in the crisis years of the 1690s and early 1700s. This analysis can be shown to have influenced very many of the contributors to the "condition of Scotland" debate in those years, and its leading themes can then be traced onwards into the thought of the Scottish Enlightenment later in the eighteenth century.

The suggestion that Fletcher be regarded as a key figure in the history of the Scottish Enlightenment has since been taken up by several scholars, notably George Davie. But it has also met with a surprising amount of resistance in some Scottish historical circles. In part the sceptics can point to the work of recent historians of the Union, headed by P.W.J. Riley, whose detailed political narratives show Fletcher to have had little influence on the actual course of events. (Although William Ferguson, otherwise close to Riley, has continued to insist on the importance of Fletcher's ideas.) But there have also been objections that Fletcher was intellectually as well as politically marginal, and that truly Scottish theological and jurisprudential traditions of thought were more important to the origins of the Scottish Enlightenment than anything sullied by association with English republicanism. The point that classical republicanism was not the sole intellectual source of the Scottish Enlightenment can of course be taken. But (quite apart from the question whether Scottish theology and jurisprudence were purely native,) the fear that Andrew Fletcher's thinking was compromised by familiarity with English writers is simply misplaced. Fletcher did have interesting English friends, John Locke among them; and he did join intellectual forces with radical English Whig critics of the standing army in the 1690s. But his writings differ markedly from those of the English Whigs, being both more historical and more European in their perspective, as well as being constantly alert to the Scottish dimension of the problems they discussed. There is indeed more intellectual craft and energy in Fletcher's works than in those of any English political writer of the period, Locke excepted; and Locke was a political philosopher, Fletcher a political analyst.

What has emerged from recent scholarship on Fletcher is thus, quite simply, a new recognition of his intelligence. Eccentric he could be, but he knew an enormous amount about European history and affairs, and he wrote about them with notable sophistication. Recognition of Fletcher's intellectual stature, of course, still leaves scholars with much to do. What is now needed is a proper intellectual biography, one which will not only recount the facts of his life, but elucidate the education, the reading and above all the experiences which formed his intelligence. Such an intellectual biography will be difficult to achieve, especially in the absence of a substantial corpus of correspondence. We need to know much more about his education in Scotland at the hands of the minister of Saltoun, Gilbert Burnet, and possibly at Edinburgh University; and we need to know about his relation to Scottish political and intellectual circles, especially after 1689, when he returned from exile abroad. Equally, we need to discover what we can about his connections with English radicals and republicans, whom he joined for Monmouth's rebellion in 1685, and with whom he is presumed to have associated in the 1690s - though historians who have studied English radicalism in this period in some detail appear to have come upon Fletcher only rarely and in passing.

Most important - and probably most difficult - of all, we need to know about Fletcher's European experiences during his exiles in the 1680s and on later travels. His exiles are said to have taken him first to the Netherlands to join those planning Monmouth's rebellion. Following his hasty departure from that expedition he fled to Spain, where tradition has it that he travelled incognito, and then went on to Hungary, where he fought with the Habsburg armies against the Turk, before finally making his way back to the United Provinces, and thence to Scotland. But these stories ought to be confirmed, and his itinerary plotted more exactly. Late in life we know that he visited Amsterdam and Paris as well as London: again it would be interesting to know how regularly he travelled after 1689.

The most formative of these experiences are likely to have been those of exile in the 1680s. For most of that time Fletcher may well have been in military service, but soldiering was not then incompatible with the intellectual life. Quite the reverse: though the subject has yet to attract the research it deserves, the military camps of early modern Europe offered thoroughly cosmopolitan company, and would have given intelligent, educated gentlemen considerable opportunity for intellectual activity and cultural exchange. As an intellectually-minded soldier exile, Fletcher compares with such contemporaries as Johann von Patkul, leader of the Livonian (modern Latvian) nobility's resistance to the imperial rule of the Swedish monarchy in the 1680s and 1690s. In due course, the fruits of Fletcher's travels were gathered in his magnificent library, which contained books acquired from all over Europe. Through a reconstruction of the library catalogue, it may be possible to establish where Fletcher bought his books, and thus to shed light on where he had been. But while the library may provide clues, it would be far better if research in the archives of Europe were to yield positive sightings of Fletcher on his travels.

If there is much still to be learnt about Fletcher, enough has nevertheless been done for a fresh assessment of his achievement to emerge. What follows is my own attempt at such an assessment. It takes as its basis Fletcher's response to the crisis facing Scotland in the ten years or so preceding the Union of 1707, the period in which all his known writings were published: whatever his contributions to the history of republicanism, or to the intellectual origins of the Scottish Enlightenment, what Fletcher himself cared about, passionately, was the condition and the liberty of Scotland. If his thought often transcended purely Scottish circumstances, those circumstances were always its inspiration. As he himself put it in an exchange with an English antagonist, it was "the insuperable difficulty I found of making my country happy by any other way", which led him to those discoveries which "have no other tendency than to render, not only my own country, but all mankind as happy as the imperfections of human nature will admit." It need only be added that my purpose is not the simplistic one of reversing Fletcher's existing reputations. His patriotism remains unquestionable and unquestioned; and while his proposal to enslave the poor of Scotland may be better explained, it cannot be unsaid. My point is rather that a fuller, more genuinely historical understanding of Fletcher's achievement is the least that is due to his intelligence and intellectual sophistication. And such a historical understanding may also - as I shall conclude by suggesting - enable us to derive from Fletcher's work more substantial insights into our own, present concerns.

The crisis facing Scotland in the years before and after 1700 was first economic and then political, and in its political dimension both British and European in scope. The economic crisis was the result of a double disaster in the late 1690s: a series of harvest failures, leading to dearth and even famine in parts of Scotland; and the collapse of the venture to establish a Scottish trading colony at Darien in Panama. The political crisis concerned Scotland's future relation to England should Queen Anne die without heir, and dynastic failure end the existing Union of the Crowns. In both countries this probability was viewed in the European framework of the actual crisis over the succession to the Spanish throne, a crisis which was in danger of ending in the French take-over of all the Spanish monarchy's territories, giving Louis XIV a virtually "universal monarchy" over Europe. It was to protect themselves against that danger that England's rulers, and many of Scotland's, came quickly to the conclusion that a new and closer union between their two kingdoms was essential.

Andrew Fletcher's response to these developments was expressed in a series of pamphlets and speeches published between 1698 and 1704, and later collected in his *Political Works*. Through these writings can be traced three fundamental convictions. First came the need to develop the Scottish economy and transform the social order. For all his personal austerity (except in the purchase of books), Fletcher was determined that the Scots as a people should no longer be poor. If anything, his *Two Discourses concerning the Affairs of Scotland* (1698) exaggerated the scale of the contemporary crisis, the better to underline the urgency of reform. Trade had become the golden ball for which all nations contended, yet the Scots alone had excluded themselves from the competition. Scottish agriculture was wholly unimproved. Fletcher's remedies were as draconian as these diagnoses were over-dramatic. Capital and land as well as labour were were all to be compulsorily re-directed for the benefit of trade and agriculture. (The enslavement of the poor, therefore, was only one part of a plan for a command economy.) Such *dirigisme* reveals Fletcher to have had a - by then - unfashionably hostile attitude towards the workings of the market; almost certainly his proposals reflect a classical preference for a clearly stratified social order, and for the pursuit of wealth as a public not a private good. But they were none the less radical in their social implications: Fletcher was clearly saying that the existing, still largely feudal social structure of Scotland must be overthrown. If Fletcher would enslave the poor, he would also destroy the power of the great lords.

Most of the other commentators on Scotland's economic condition (they included William Paterson, John Law and William Seton) had more confidence in the market. But they shared and in several instances clearly took from Fletcher both his sense of the urgency of the crisis and his radical hostility to the existing social structure. Moreover, they continued to disagree among themselves about the extent to which Scotland should simply be exposed to the workings of the market in its trading relations with its neighbours. Fletcher's proposals might be regarded as eccentrically extreme, but he was also seen to be sounding a timely warning about the dangers facing the economy of a backward, outlying country when it was joined to that of a larger, more advanced neighbour. The market, Fletcher insisted, was perfectly capable of reinforcing the concentration of resources in the metropolitan centre, in London and the South East, at the expense of Scotland.

As it was, Scotland already stood in a position of shameful political dependence on London. By depriving Scotland of its king and his court, Fletcher told the Scottish parliament in 1703, the Union of the Crowns had reduced the nation to a condition "more like a conquered province than a free independent people." But Fletcher's response to this situation was not a simple call for a restoration of Scottish independence. Instead, he sought to persuade the Scottish Parliament to agree to strict constitutional "Limitations" upon the power of any future monarch of Scotland who was shared with England. These Limitations were designed to secure the independence of the Scottish Parliament and Judiciary, while enabling Scotland to continue to enjoy the defence advantages of an equal, confederal union with England.

Through the proposal of these Limitations Fletcher voiced the second of what I have suggested were three fundamental convictions: that the Scots must secure their liberty by creating for themselves a viable political community. In form the Limitations harked back to the programme of the Covenanters in 1641. But it is clear that Fletcher had little time for old war cries (especially religious ones), and scant regard for Scotland's supposed "ancient constitution". With whatever justice, he believed that Scottish politics before 1603 had consisted of no more than the feuds and wars of an over-mighty nobility; and that since 1603 that nobility had been but the hired instruments of the English court. In the political as in the social sphere, therefore, Fletcher sought radical, structural change. Nothing less than a re-founding of Scotland's political institutions, and, still more important, a genuine willingness among Scots to take responsibility for them, would be required.

Here Fletcher was at his most profoundly republican. His point was not that the Scots should dispense with their monarchy (though he himself had no time for the hereditary principle); but that they must see the need to take political responsibility for themselves, accommodating their political and religious differences in order to create a true political community. It was the ideal of the ancient *polis*, whose citizens might have different qualities and values, but were none the less willing to participate together in the community's government and defence. (In line with the ancient *polis*, it was also, of course, an ideal which presupposed the exclusion of the servile, labouring poor from active citizenship.) Fletcher's view of the Scottish past implied that the Scots had never really formed such a political community: his speeches of 1703 conveyed the message that unless and until they did, their relation 'to the English would remain one of dependence.

Precisely because Fletcher's message was so radical, it was too demanding for most of his contemporaries to accept. It can even be said to have strengthened the case of those who advocated a closer, incorporating union with England. The arguments of these incorporating unionists were more sophisticated than is often supposed: while they too emphasised the supposed confusion of Scottish political life before 1603, they were quick to expose the difficulty of realising any new scheme such as Fletcher's. Far easier, they suggested, to join the already strong and successful English political community, and to be incorporated into its parliament at Westminster. Even when faced with these arguments, however, Fletcher made no attempt to compromise. Instead he proceeded to radicalise his position still further, by elaborating his third and most ambitious conviction: that any lasting solution to the problem of Scotland's relation to England must involve a more general reform of government across the whole continent of Europe.

In *An Account of a Conversation concerning a Right Regulation of Governments for the common good of Mankind* (1704), Fletcher suggested that geography had divided Europe naturally into ten portions, and that each of these ought to contain a union of ten to twelve states. These unions Fletcher envisaged as strict confederations, with sovereignty being retained by the constituent city-states or principalities. To be understood, this plan needs to be read in the context of an earlier work, the *Discorso delle cose di Spagna (Discourse of the Affairs of Spain)*, which Fletcher published, in Italian and with the imprint "Napoli" in 1698. In the *Discorso* Fletcher had canvassed the prospects for a Universal Monarchy in Europe as a result of the Spanish Succession Crisis. The obvious candidate to be such a monarch was Louis XIV, but Fletcher feared that William III had such aspirations too, now that he was king of England as well as Stadtholder in Holland. It was this threat of Universal Monarchy that the proposal for a Europe of confederal unions was designed to meet. It was almost certainly inspired by the example of the confederal unions which had successfully resisted the great monarchies of seventeenth-century Europe, including the League of Swiss Cantons, the Polish-Lithuanian Commonwealth and, most successful of all, the United Provinces of the Netherlands. On Fletcher's plan the British kingdoms would thus form one confederal union on the same basis as all the others: in effect, he was saying, there should be a United Provinces rather than a United Kingdom of Great Britain.

To extend the principle of confederal union beyond Britain to Europe was not, of course, to diminish its difficulty. Quite the reverse: Fletcher's plan

Portrait of Andrew Fletcher of Saltoun
courtesy of the National Galleries of Scotland

would have required a constant commitment on the part of the provincial components of each union to check the aggrandising ambitions of royal courts and the capital cities which housed them. The Scots themselves would have had to make common cause with the many other European nations which had hitherto been provincial dependencies of greater monarchies - with the Catalans and the Neapolitans, with the Livonians and the Hungarians. It was an astonishing vision, one rooted in Fletcher's own wide experience of Europe, yet imagining an almost complete reversal of the existing political order. To have realised it would have taken a wave of revolts and revolutions the length and breadth of Europe, sweeping away the several imperial monarchies - Swedish, Austrain, Spanish and French - which then dominated the continent.

In the end, therefore, the application of Fletcher's intelligence to Scotland's predicament led to what might well seem utopian conclusions. In the Scottish context, it was almost as if Fletcher was admitting that there was no immediate, no purely Scottish alternative to the form of union which the English wished to impose. Although he continued vehemently to oppose incorporating union, doing his best to disrupt the last Scottish Parliament as it voted through the clauses of the Union Treaty, his own proposals were disregarded, and he probably did not write on them again. (A pamphlet of 1706, *State of the Controversy betwixt United and Separate Parliaments*, has often been attributed to him, most recently by P.H. Scott, but the attribution remains doubtful.) By 1707 the role of the Patriot did indeed seem the only one left for him to play.

That Fletcher's political career ended in failure should not, however, lead us to regard his achievement in purely intellectual terms. His writings on the condition of Scotland in the years around 1700 have a significance beyond their analytical quality. By seizing on the crisis facing the country as an opportunity for a radical reappraisal of its economic, social and political structures, Fletcher had contrived to set the agenda for the creation of a genuine Scottish political community. To vindicate a nation's independence, he realised, it was not enough to invoke the names and deeds of its ancestors. A viable political community required the building of new institutions, and a willingness to be responsible for them. This the Scots must do for themselves. At the same time, Fletcher had recognised in the crisis of the Spanish Succession the necessarily broader, European framework of the Scots' predicament. If their own freedom and independence were to be secure, the Scots would have to participate in the construction of a new political order in Europe as a whole: an order based on the equality of many small nations, not on the preoponderance of a few great powers. So radical an agenda might be well beyond the capacity of Fletcher's fellow Scots to take seriously, let alone put into practice, pressed as they were by English threats and bribes, and reassured by the existence of a well-argued Scottish case for the Union. What matters, however, is that the agenda existed, that the possibility of a Scottish political community within a new European order was set before them: this was the achievement of Andrew Fletcher's political intelligence.

*

Circumstances have changed enormously between Fletcher's time and our own: Scots have both gained and lost as partners in the British state and its empire. But since whatever else they may have gained, they have still not constituted themselves as a political community, Fletcher's agenda for the attainment of that crucial objective remains very much to the point. The essential requirements of a Scottish political community are those on which Fletcher insisted: the achievement of institutional self-sufficiency, activated by the willingness of citizens to take responsibility for their institutions while respecting their political differences. Over the past two decades, moreover, circumstances within and outwith Scotland have begun to offer positive encouragement to a restatement of Fletcher's case. It is on the construction of such a political community that the Campaign for a Scottish Assembly has embarked; and what distinguishes this initiative from that for Devolution in the 1970s is that the scale of the challenge has at last been recognised. Not only are new political institutions being devised, but the public support without which they cannot be brought into existence is beginning to be mobilised.

The CSA nevertheless faces major obstacles in realising Fletcher's object- ive. These are not simply the legacy of vested interests built up over the 300 years of the existing Union; nor are they simply products of the present government's conviction that the concentration of power in London is the prerequisite of national prosperity and "greatness". For a modern, democratic political community is structurally different from the one Fletcher envisaged, in that a modern democracy, as distinct from a classical republic, presupposes the extension of citizenship to all classes of society. Further, the commonly accepted means for the expression of political interests within a democratic community is a competitive party system. Once a party system is in place, there is a natural tendency for the parties to identify the interests they represent and the interests of the community as one and the same. The tendency is only re-inforced by an electoral system in which the winner takes all: the temptation of exclusive power held out by such a system is one to which no democratic party either possessing or plausibly aspiring to majority support can be immune. As the party now enjoying this support in Scotland, Labour is bound to regard self-government as a favour for it to bestow, on terms which will preserve its power; as periodically plausible aspirants to majority support, the Nationalists would like to imagine that the winning of Scottish independence and their own accession to power can be achieved at one and the same simple stroke. But no party can constitute a political community on its own: the process of creating a new community requires a consensus transcending the competitive pursuit of power, and the latter needs to be at least partially suspended for the sake of the former. The problem is already damagingly apparent in the parties' responses to the Campaign for a Scottish Assembly: if it is to be overcome, constituting the political com- munity must, as Fletcher argued, be given priority.

If this is the moment to recall and insist on Fletcher's agenda for a Scottish political community, how much more is it the time to recall his vision of Europe. Over the 1980s the recognition that Scotland belongs in Europe has provided increasingly good reason to renew the argument for self-government. Not only was the EEC visibly undermining the absolute sovereignty of Westminster, it offered the Scots a framework within which to claim more autonomy without risking economic isolation. But in itself this has been to use Europe as no more than a pretext: Fletcher's point in 1704 was that unless small nations such as Scotland deliberately combined to establish a new political order throughout Europe, greater powers would continue to dominate the continent, and England would be free to go on dominating Scotland. Given the structure of the EEC, this danger is very real: the integration of Europe proceeds on French and German terms, under a strongly federal, centralised EEC. A separate Scottish presence within the EEC, aligning itself with the smaller nations of the community, is thus desirable in its own right, representing a more constructive response to Franco-German predominance than Mrs Thatcher's little Englander obstructiveness.

Truly radical possibilities, however, have been created by the extraordinary revolutions of 1989. As an empire comparable to those of the 17th century European monarchies has been swept away, the smaller nations of central Europe have re-emerged on the stage. The outcome of their revolutions is, as yet, still open. Many of these nations face formidable difficulties in establishing free institutions, and in transcending historic religious and ethnic differences, sufficient to form stable political communities. Even if they do, it is likely that German reunification will lead to a single German state whose resources would enable it to replace Russia's hegemony over Central Europe with its own, using a federal EEC as its cover. Likely, but not necessary: Germany actually has a much longer political history as a confederation of distinct regional territories within the old Holy Roman Empire. In these circumstances, the point of Andrew Fletcher's vision of Europe suddenly seems quite clear: there is now an opportunity to form a Europe of regions and smaller nations, confederally united on terms calculated to prevent the emergence of any new imperial power. The challenge to constitute a Scottish political community that will help to form such a Europe, the most ambitious of the challenges which Fletcher set his contemporaries, has finally become ours.   John Robertson.

Bibliography:

The Political Works of Andrew Fletcher (editions of 1732, 1737 and 1749); Andrew Fletcher: Selected Political Writings and Speeches, ed. David Daiches (1979). G.W.T. Omond, Fletcher of Saltoun, Famous Scots series (1897); W.C. Mackenzie, Andrew Fletcher of Saltoun, His Life and Times (1935); J.G.A. Pocock, The Machiavellian Moment. Florentine Political Thought and the Atlantic Republican Tradition (1975); N.T. Phillipson, 'The Scottish Enlightenment', in The Enlightenment in National Context ed. R. Porter & M. Teich (1981); G.E. Davie. The Scottish Enlightenment; Historical Association (1981); P.W.J. Riley, The Union of England and Scotland (1978); W. Ferguson, Scotland's Relations with England: a Survey to 1707 (1977); J.C. Robertson, 'Andrew Fletcher's Vision of Union', in Scotland and England 1286-1815 ed. R.A.Mason (1987).

Jenny Robertson

OLD PARISH KIRK

The place where people prayed is overgrown
with grass and thistle, a neglected shell
where criss-cross ivy buttresses thick stone:
a scaffolding of branch and leaf and wall.

Exposed to gale and sun on its green hill
this roofless kirk keeps always open door.
Three glassless windows face the Sound of Mull;
dense weeds, knee-high, invade, in hordes, its floor.

To build the kirkyard stonework was displaced,
and, buried here, the landlord's hated tool.
"When you are dead," a homeless woman cursed,
"let nettles prove the devil has your soul."

The tacksman's grave bears witness to that doom,
land and kirk are barren as his tomb.

PARISH KIRK (CONTEMPORARY)

So John and Morag bring their babe to kirk
to be baptised; and sea and sky wear lace
to mark the day. Cars back and queue to park,
for birth shows continuity of place,
and pews are packed, though galleries are blocked
where minister and gentry once were raised
above douce Sunday-suited crofting folk.
Today the child, sign in which we trace
our source, is in the midst; all white and pink
she yells as water drops upon her face -
to great goodwill. She is a living link
whose name is in the Gaelic of her race
which kirk and commerce can no longer speak:
the heritage is hers, as hers the grace.

NATURE STUDY, 1910

Schoolchildren crossed bay and bog
with a crowdie piece, a well cut peat
(that ancient mix of bog and heather root),
sometimes went out along the shore
for Nature Study, which may lend
more brightness than scratch of chalk on slate,

rhyming Dick Whittington, that lad o' pairts -
and what's the use of golden streets
to bairns whose bare feet cross silver sand,
who watch white breakers rise and roar?

"Come, children!"
Miss Taylor's perfect English
lacks the music Gaeldom gives the Southern tongue.

"It is the flowering season, we must collect
our specimens, classify, select
watergowan, violet,
clover, heather, foxglove, broom,
return then to our own schoolroom,
draw our flowers, note each name."

Miss Taylor, reared in Morningside
teaches children who will soon
serve maritime and landed wealth,
nurse, teach, increase the Glasgow police:

leave the croft, the hill, the burn.

Miss Taylor recites Tennyson,
instructs in basic hygiene
girls whose great grandmothers, illiterate,
knew by rote cure and lore,
could prepare
toad to heal dropsy, worm for gout,
boil shell-fish, cormorant, limpet
to fill the flesh of thin changelings:

there are no children in that schoolhouse now.

CILLE-MHOIRE

Marked out as if for children's play
with a wall which runs all round,
St. Mary's bield with burial place
has vanished underground.

The kyries and psalms are dumb,
no chime of sanctus bells
now bend folk low like grass in hairst;
yet endless water wells

from some unknown and secret source,
some undiscovered cause,
with no regard for chance nor change,
obeying its own laws,

to fill the font, a hollowed stone,
unused but never dry,
where those who lie beneath this grass
took naming with a cry.

Round, with wetness at its core
for questing hand or mouth,
like lodestar constant in its task,
this vessel rinses drouth.

Jenny Robertson

Harry Smart

POEMS FROM SHOAH

Shoah is a Hebrew word, meaning 'destruction', and used to name the Holocaust. The poems here are from a sequence of around fifty, which form an imaginative reconstruction of the flood story in Genesis. Although characters, places and incidents from the Holocaust underlie many of the poems, references to historical events are oblique or parabolic.

THE PROSECUTOR STATES HIS CASE

I have flown the earth,
Considering.
I have leapt
To claim my own.

I am bright in sunlight,
Darkness in deep places.

I saw, in those first days,
The gold and the onyx,

I know the scent of aromatic resins,
The sweet river airs were mine.

How that whirling sword
Touched my heart.

Now I am become
My true free self,

Now I may take the stage,
May roar and fall

Upon the sons of men
As winter, pitiless.

My time is short, I have only a season,
But how well I carry off the light.

DOVE WARMS HERSELF IN THE ARK'S KITCHEN

Looking at the oven
Dove considers the warmth of it, the silence
Of the iron within which the fire burns,
The iron stability of fact.

She turns and watches the timbers
Not moving one against the other, unresisting
As a nail is thumped into the hull to hold a coat.
She is glad of this shelter, of this dry, warm place

Which offers her neutrality, used for kindness.
She is glad of wood pushed unresisting into fire.
This place had a rough making, and a launching
Without prayers for blessing. This place sailed out

On terror, on clawing desperation, on total bitterness
And now it sails, it is observed,
No more.
Beyond the hull the water is observed

To be gentle, though Dove had heard hymns
Of violence, taken its heart to be demonic.
Dove sees the man sitting at the table
Silently, incapable of action, simply being what he is.

A MEMORY OF WHITE WATER

We passed through water whitened
By almond blossom,
By branches white with almond blossom
shaken from the trees'
Last flowering for funeral.

I remembered how my God had said
You will see how harshly,
You will see how harshly
I will deal with all my enemies
Who say they did not know me.

I remember how I wondered
Who is my neighbour now?
Who is my neighbour now
That I have no-one but my family
Who say they do not know me?

IT WAS LATE

Evening in the kitchen, and I sat quietly beside the stove,
Still warm, and fed the child. Only the two of us
Still awake, the air was clear of piety
And silences. I heard his breathing, heard

The warm shawl rustling as he moved
And heard the healthy suck of him at me.
I felt him warm as kisses, toothless
Confidence of feeding. We'd cried

Through weeks of cracked skin till we learned
Together how to manage this. Quiet, comfortable
As the night that he was made, and warm
As love in memory, yet new, and every day new

Things that he learned were wonderful. He knew
Nothing of totality, nothing of the spirit of the age,
But he had learned to stand, to hold the chair's edge
And to stand. To hold my hand and stand upon his own two feet.
He broke from feeding, milk-drops on his lips, smiling

At me. In all the world I knew I'd made him.
That same day, in the newly summered weather
We'd watched this boy's father
Take his own life, as we thought, in his hands.

We'd watched him dive into the sea, watched
His white flesh nail itself to darkness
Underneath the water, disappearing
For that one moment when time stopped

And no-one said a thing. We cheered him
As he surfaced, as he waved. We laughed
Because we didn't know what else to do
And cried when he had climbed on board again.

DOVE TOYS UNWITTINGLY WITH HERESY

She waits on a low branch for the fog to clear.
She sees a good place for a nest
But the water is still too near.

Dove has meditated on the fragile shell,
Has watched a dove's egg broken,
But she cannot describe her own contents. Well,

She has listened often enough to the old man's piety,
Not comprehending *nephesh* and temples,
Life, hope, materiality.

A sent wave splashes her wing.
She shakes the water from her feathers,
Looks up, sees that the mist is lifting.

She opens her wing and considers each quill,
Light and air pass through
Yet there is a membrane still.

Dove considers the mist, stares at it,
Sees it thinned to mere invisibility.
Thin, says dove, as the Holy Spirit.

YAHWEH IS A WARRIOR

He sets his bow in the heavens,
Shows his fire-bright war-bow
Arc, taut.

Such arrows that bow would cast,
Says the man,
Though aimed at heaven.

He bows his head,
This water has been like coals to his mouth.
So he has been favoured. He has survived.

I will not destroy the world again,
Says the message,
By water.

Dove, light-ringed, is free at last;
She circles from the ark
But turns to look back

From the distance.
The boat is a hollowed skull
Charred and swollen. *Metanoia*;

Jewelled breath, sunlit dew.
New meadows hear
Dove's wood-flute call.

Harry Smart

3010: A Space Idiocy
Marsha Prescod

There's no point asking me how I got here, because I don't know. I'm as ignorant as you are regarding the details. One minute I was walking down the road in the 20th century, next minute I'm walking down the road in the 31st century. Don't know whether its a hallucination, a road accident, a dream, death, someone else's fantasy or what. No blinding flashes, or little green men to give me some kind of explanation. Nothing. I'm just here.

Been here for about, oh, six or seven months. Not sure of the geography - things have changed a hell of a lot. Nobody I met was particularly taken aback, they just took me to some kind of, I don't know, hospital? Rehabilitation centre? Church? Hard to say just what, but I was kitted out in clothes that were more contemporary (so that I wouldn't scare the children) and a bunch of people quite willingly volunteered themselves as friends, minders, whatever. It seemed very spontaneous, but looking back, everything happened so easily that it really must have been a result of a highly-organised operation. So, here I am. How I've managed not to go bananas I really don't know.

Now I know what you are saying. Why the hell doesn't he get on with telling us what its like instead of pissing about with his personal problems? What's it like in a thousand years' time? Is the sky still blue? Are Milwall still as vile? Or did everything get nuked out of existence, reduced to primaeval slime?

Well, the first thing I'll tell you is to be patient. Things are very relaxed here. I don't really know too much myself, so all I can do is tell you things as they were told to me.

Like I remember asking Yinka while we were sitting with a group of people in her house and she was showing us a particularly elaborately-plaited hairstyle. I asked her - fill me in on what's happened in the last couple of hundred years. She, along with everybody else, smiled and looked vague, and changed the subject almost as if I'd said something indecent. However, later on in the evening she gathered me up and zipped me over to a friend's house (zip is the simplest way I know how to describe the mode of transport, though if you've seen Star Trek with its 'beam-me-up-Scotty', that will give you some idea of what I mean, though it's more mental than physical). She introduced me to her friend using a word which would translate into English as 'someone who is hungry (for knowledge)'. Oh yes. One thing about this century is that English is very much a dead language. There are five to seven Global Languages of an International Nature (GLINs) which everyone speaks, but English is not one of them. It's not even the ancestor of one of them. The GLINs are descended from Mandarin Chinese, Hindi, Wolof, Arabic and Navajo as the main ones.

This friend of Yinka's surprised me. First off, he was *white*. I got all excited at this but when I tried to draw him into some sense of feeling kinship with me, he looked startled, then not too pleased. I checked myself then, and made the customary greeting rituals (which in the exitement I'd forgotten to perform) and waited for him to signal to me to 'rest and receive'. That's the best way to describe what happens when people visit, because it's more than just sitting. When he saw my discomfort, Yinka's friend - his name was Yao - became as warm and friendly as possible, to put me at my ease. One thing you notice with these people straight away is that they are very open, direct. I saw a look pass between him and Yinka (I think the people of this century are either semi-telepathic or empathic) and intuition told me that she'd brought me here not because she couldn't answer my questions, but because she thought I'd be more comfortable if *he* did. This was true, but made me feel very ashamed.

Yao, she explained to me, was a . . . she used a word which in translation would mean something like historian/griot/medium. Hard to explain. There were many people like him, keepers of records who seemed able to walk around with a vast body of knowledge in their heads. This puzzled me because writing (albeit not a type that I could read) definitely existed, but these record-keepers took precedence. "Please tell me," I stammered, "as much as you know about what happened between the 1980s and now. Everything's so . . . different. I'd really like to know how this present civilisation came about."

He did his best. He told me everything he knew. Later on, after I'd learnt the rudiments of one of the GLINs, I went to one of the biggest libraries and looked it up, and the information was substantially the same, though I found that he had provided details the books didn't have.

First off, it wasn't clear whether or not there had been a nuclear war. Something big had happened - of that there was no doubt because there was so little information surviving from the 20th century, so their archaeologists often had to make wild guesses regarding period artefacts that were found from time to time. Also there were certain areas that everyone avoided - rates of illness were higher there, and plant and animal life either strange in some way or non-existent. But in this century they had no concept of the atom or nuclear weapons, though they seemed to have some source of power or fuel that was both efficient and abundant. In many places I saw a sign that looked reminiscent of the CND symbol, and areas where it appeared or people who wore it were particularly revered. When I asked why, the explanation was so mystical that I couldn't understand. Our century - the 20th - was seen as barbaric. Partly because of the gross misinterpretation of their social scientists. For instance, he told me that the mass torture and cannibalism that had gripped the world for hundreds of years had been eradicated. When I asked him what this meant, he showed me a hologram of some charred documents in their equivalent of a museum. There was a picture of Christ on the Cross, and underneath there was the phrase which he translated correctly as "this is my body, and this is my blood. Eat and drink in remembrance of me." With a stunned sensation, I realised that they were taking some of the words of the mass quite literally. But my command of GLINs wasn't sophisticated enough to explain. He refused therefore to believe that it was a religious ceremony. In fact, he said, the religion of the 20th century had grown larger and more powerful for at least another century until it had a total command of the world, but then had rapidly and inexplicably declined in somewhere around the 22nd century, just prior to the dawning of the New Age.

Startled, I asked him what he meant. He zipped me over to a place which contained fragments of celluloid, and there I was shown a pastiche of excerpts from Hollywood films, all jumbled together, some as short as 30 seconds. He told me that they had found temples to these Gods everywhere, relics of their shrines too. He showed me one. Though mostly a twisted heap of metal, I was just able to decipher a worn inscription bearing the name 'Pye' which made me burst into ironic laughter. "A TV set!" I exclaimed as Yao and Yinka looked on kindly. No doubt they thought the savage was glad to find a comforting symbol of his primative religious beliefs. I just thought how fitting it was that Marilyn Monroe (whom they solemnly described to me as the senior Goddess of my time) was finally deified. I started to feel a little crazy then. Crazier when they took me through to a gallery where they said a typical religious ceremony from my time had been recreated. I found huge holograms that flashed what looked like either a football match or an athletics meeting - both images were in there - and images of huge crowds roaring and jumping to their feet. The last flash was of a film star (Ronald Reagan) speaking solemnly on a dais in front of a huge fire - the Olympic Flame.

Yinka and Yao then zipped me back to his place to rest and receive again. I certainly needed to rest - I was starting to feel nauseous. I'd been prepared to hear some horrific tale of war, pestilence or cataclysm that had swallowed up the world, but at least that there would be *something*. Not this huge gap, this void, illuminated by garbled misinterpretations of trivia. "What happened to America, to Russia, to the East-West power struggle?" I asked Yao. He looked pensive. "America . . ." he said slowly. "Yes," I said. "I know the land masses now are different, but even so you must know about the leaders of these countries?"

"Oh yes," he said, and rattled off a whole stream of names such as James Brown, Aretha Franklin, The Beatles, Elvis Presley, and others that I was not familiar with. From his description of our complex and inadequate electoral system, I finally realised that some magazines with the pop music charts from 1956 to 1976 had survived, and had been interpreted as political documents. The fact that records of the artists survived here and there didn't dissuade the people of the 31st century of this notion, because artistic people had an exalted place among them, and music was as important a means of communication as the GLINs.

"You've got it all wrong!" I shouted. "Didn't you read any of the books you found?" They looked at me in that sad yet kindly way you'd look at anyone who was completely off his chump. "You're hurting," Yinka said. "Let's stop now. Rest and receive." Yao pointed out that, firstly, the materials of my time (he meant paper) had not survived very well. Then, too, it seemed that they found our writings as hard to interpret as we had found Egyptian hieroglyphics. The translation he'd given me of the phrase in the book on Christ, for example, had taken him several years to work out. Also, archaeologists studying artefacts from the period from the 16th to the 22nd centuries - it was very much lumped together as the age of the barbarians - were only able to work on them for limited periods at a time, as they found the morals and values of those times deeply distressing. I went beetroot red at that. Yao and Yinka were speaking to me across the divide of five hundred years, from a civilisation that is highly spiritual, environmentalist and ritualistic. I must have seemed as brutish to them as a Cro-Magnon man would seem to you and me.

Yao said that they knew a lot about the wars of the Northern tribes (he meant World Wars I & II - although they had the manic idea that Hitler was an entertainer of some kind). Much study had also been done of a period they referred to as the Great Tragedy, The Endless Holocaust, The Ultimate Terror. I took this to mean the extermination camps of the 1930s and 40s, but it turned out to mean the destruction of the Indians of North, South and Central America, and of the Aboriginal peoples of Australasia. Also, the periods of the slave trade and the conquest of India, Africa and Asia. I'd never condoned all that, of course, but our history books don't dwell on it the way these people do. Seen through their eyes, that whole period of expansion, exploration and empire seemed like one giant bloodbath.

It seemed that the pain of those ages had survived in living memory, in a way that Shakespeare, Descartes, Wittgenstein, Nietzche had not.

I felt as if my brain was imploding. We had to stop there, and both Yao and Yinka were adamant that they didn't think further enlightenment would be good for my psyche, but I had to know. So, after a few hours, the discussion resumed. I don't know what was more terrible, the things I was being told, or the calm certainty with which they were delivered. The way a whole era was dismissed - to oblivion.

The world as you and I know it was finally brought to an end when the mass psychosis of the psychopathic Northern tribes (yes, that's how he described Western society to me) caused a total spiritual collapse, during which all social order broke down. To illustrate what he meant, Yao showed me a mental image of something that was rather fuzzy. it looked like excerpts from a hard-core porn magazine, showing explicit gynaecological shots of women of various ages and sizes. In the 31st century, many - though not all - societies are matrilineal, and there are parallel institutions (church, juciciary, parliament) for each sex. The Head of State is either the Queen Mother or the King Father, with a mostly female electorate picking the members of both male and female ruling institutions. Pornography of the kind enjoyed in my age therefore was unthinkable. In fact, matters relating to sex and sexuality were very private. The people I met were tactile and affectionate. To me, they projected a lot of sex appeal, but I was never able to ask them about the subject. Thus I had no common reference point from which to start to explain what Yao showed me. His people could only understand such a phenomenon, therefore, in terms suggesting the mental derangement of an entire society. Confusion. Total confusion.

Under Yao and Yinka's sympathetic gaze I broke down and wept.

Marsha Prescod

Kole Omotoso

Strange Bedfellows

The alliance between Shagari's NPN and Azikiwe's NPP mocked in its repetition of it the alliance between Balewa's NPC and Azikawe's NCNC. 1959. 1979. Twenty years stood between them, twenty years and nothing really had changed. Except that as the alliance of 1959 approached another election in 1964 and collapsed, the one of 1979 approached 1983 and broke down. Also, by 1964, the NPC was beginning to think of ruling the country alone as a one-party state. In 1983, NPN was not thinking of it; they were saying they were going to run the country alone as a one-party state forever.

The system which the Obasanjo military government left behind for Shagari to work would have benefited a new nation-wide upper-middle-class, especially of people from the military. The system is premised on the belief that if there are enough rich men in society, the poor would have no problem scraping through life, with the aid of the crumbs from the tables of the affluent. It was not that the Shagari crew did not believe in this theory. Only they were far more anxious than Obasanjo and company thought, to become rich men in their turn. And to become rich men, they did not require the system to work. In fact they had to sabotage it. And to sabotage the system and remain in power they had also to prepare their own power base within the armed forces. Inside and outside of the armed forces there were enough people interested in the survival of the status quo to stand up in defence of it. Thus, by the time the preparations were being made towards the elections of 1983, the NPN had the army to defeat, not the other five registered political parties. But it was the preparation for defeating the five political parties that got all the attention in the Nigerian media.

Sometime in 1982, the different state secretaries of the NPN instructed any of their members aspiring to the position of candidate for the gubernatorial elections to deposit any sum of money between 25,000 naira and 50,000 naira at the party headquarters in Lagos. There were 171 prospective aspirants in the NPN party alone. These were made up of incumbent governors and many challengers. In Cross-River State ten challengers withdrew out of the twelve aspirants only a few hours before the primary elections took place.

In a meeting of the National Executive of the UPN in Lagos, Chief Awolowo suggested that the incumbent governors be given another go at the job. "They need to complete their projects during their second terms," the leader of the UPN argued. But when it was put to a vote, there were dissenting voices. And so, the race for the office of governor led to grave divisions within the UPN. Chief Awolowo's attempts to get a progressive alliance to beat the NPN foundered on the rocks of mutual recrimination and personal ambition. The NPN did what they could to keep their enemies divided.

As in the first performance of 1965, the violence that would give the armed forces their excuse for coming to rule Nigeria would take place in the area covered by the old Western Region, the domain of the Yorubas. The stakes were highest here. The argument among leaders of the NPN was rather simple as far as they were concerned. A Yoruba man had been the chairman of the party from 1979, yet the greatest enemies of the party came from among the Yorubas. And in the distribution of officers, the chairman was thinking of being the presidential candidate for the party come 1987. The only way he could get it would be if he could deliver the Yorubas to the NPN.

"We shall do it!" said the chairman jumping up from his seat. "If it cannot be done in that way, we shall employ other means. The President must score at least one quarter of the votes in all the Yoruba states, and NPN gubernatorial candidates must win at least three of the four Yoruba states. That's all."

Ultimately, the contention in the Yoruba area and the contention between the armed forces and the NPN were to dovetail in the seizure of power by the armed forces in December 1983.

* * * * *

The way things were going, and in spite of good relations Mr Fagbamigbe enjoyed with the leader of the UPN, it was clear that he would not be adopted to run for the House of Representatives come 1983. The deputy-governor of Ondo State had also indicated his desire to run for the post of governor of the state in the next elections. But in view of the decision that the incumbent governors should continue, all those who aspired to challenge them were asked to withdraw their candidature. The deputy-gov-ernor refused and jumped from the UPN to the NPN along with his supporters, including Mr Fagbamigbe. The house along Methodist Road became a meeting point for the NPN in Akure and the leaders of the party in Ondo State.

Just before the Ilesha public transport motor park in Akure, there is a left turn-off. The area is not a planned housing area but there are a number of new houses there. As with most planned and unplanned housing areas in many parts of Nigeria, the roads are not graded or tarred. Off this road, another road, rougher than the first, led to a duplex. Mr Fagbamigbe came here from time to time to see a friend. One morning in May he left the house, and as he walked to his green Mercedes-Benz, a shot rang out and bounced off its roof. He looked in the direction from which he thought the shot had come. Almost immediately another shot rang out, this time whistling past his head. He dodged and hid behind the car. No further shots came. He dashed back into the house and sat down shaking visibly.

"Somebody has just tried to kill me!" he whispered hoarsely to himself. He did not even notice that his friend who was sitting next to him said nothing. After a while he got up and cautiously went out of the house. He got into his car and drove slowly out of the road and onto the main road. He thought he saw someone with a dane-gun running away when he came on to the main road. He tried to pursue the person but it was no use. He drove to his house at Methodist Church Road. He parked the car behind the other vehicles and went upstairs using the cement staircase at the back of the house. This way he was able to avoid the numerous visitors who were waiting for him in the sitting room in front of the house. He sat down in the family sitting room, his mind still at the point where he had been fired at.

"Daddy," said one of the children, rushing into the family sitting room, "there's a man from Radio Kaduna who says he wants to talk to you."

"Tell him to wait," he replied and waved the child away.

In the interview he had with Radio Kaduna that afternoon, he accused his former colleagues of the UPN for being responsible for the attempt on his life. In their response to this accusation the UPN secretariat in Akure denied the allegation and said that the explanation of the shooting was far more intricate than what Mr Fagbamigbe had revealed.

"According to information reaching us," said the UPN release, "the honourable member of the House of Representatives had been applying some traditional medicine to his body which was supposed to be capable of dissolving bullets on contact. The incident under discussion was said to be the occasion for the honourable member to test the veracity of this claim of his medicine-man. We had nothing to do with it."

Mr & Mrs Fagbamigbe were attending a funeral service at the Catholic Cathedral of the Sacred Heart School, Akure, on the afternoon of the following Sunday when his brother came looking for him and eventually got somebody to call them out of the church. "Kola, what brings you here?" he asked as they came out of the church. Kola did not answer immediately. He looked at him. He looked well and his usually beautiful mirror-smooth black skin had not in any way deteriorated. He was clean-shaven as usual and wore a light blue velvet *dansiki* and *sokoto*. His wife wore *iro* and *buba* of the same material. If he was under any stress, he did not carry it on his face.

"I came to see you and I'm going back from here."

"Why the hurry?" the wife asked him.

"I just came to see you," he repeated. "When I got to the house I was told that you were here. I need to talk to you."

"What is it?" he asked slowly, his face losing the smile that had welcomed Kola in the first place.

"I read about the shooting. I don't like it. Why did you have to join another party? Why don't you just leave this place and come to Ibadan and concentrate on your publishing. You are doing well with it, making a good name for yourself."

"He can't leave politics," the wife said simply.

"You know Chief Awolowo came to campaign here," Mr Fagbamigbe began, as if he was introducing a new dimension to the discussion without answering the series of questions which Kola had asked, and without commenting on his wife's statement.

"Yes?"

"He came to campaign, at the stadium near the LA school and you know what he said?"

"What did he say?"

"He said *E ku isehinde Fagbamigbe* - condolences on the demise of Fagbamigbe."

"Can you believe that?" asked the wife looking at her husband and then at Kola. Mr Fagbamigbe was looking intently at the horizon, avoiding Kola's eyes. "Never mind what the old man said. He must have been carried away by the political campaign rhetoric!"

"If you say so," was all that Mr Fagbamigbe responded. Then he looked back at the cathedral where the funeral service was still going on.

"Thanks for coming, Kola. If I didn't join another political party these people would have killed me. At least I have a political organisation that would defend me if they attempt to kill me."

"Who can defend you from your friends?" Kola asked and almost immediately wished he had not said it. They shook hands and he watched them both walk back into the cathedral hand in hand. He had never seen both husband and wife so close. At the door of the cathedral both of them turned back and waved to him. He waved back and turned to go to his car.

* * * * *

The presidential elections took place throughout the country on 6th August 1983. Within 48 hours after the elections, FEDECO was able to declare that the incumbent, President Shehu Shagari, had won a landslide victory for another four-year term of office. In spite of the fact that the logic of the victory of the NPN candidate for presidency should create a bandwagon effect, the NPN did not leave this to the hands of the Nigerian voters.

The gubernatorial elections in the nineteen states took place on the 13th of August, the Saturday after the presidential election. On the 10th of August, the NPN leader in Abeokuta, in Ogun State, had a meeting with his agents. It was in his house.

"We have discussed that we have people who will go round and we have given you the programme. We are discussing with groups like you all over the town," he began as soon as he had attracted their attention from the drinks. "So many votes have got to be delivered in your polling booths and you can use any method you choose to get them. Now if these people come round and vote, you count, NPN has 250 or 300 out of 500 or 400, fine. But if they do not come, or if they come and do not make up that number, you are expected to find a way to manipulate the vote. I hope you understand. I don't want to talk too much about it. Use any method that you like. Where you have a total number of registered voters on your list of up to 99 you must give us 75. When we have 100-199 voters, NPN must have 125. Where we have 300-399 voters NPN must have 175. I hope you understand. So, if you want to write it down now, take your pen and write." And he repeated the formula for them.

He resumed: "You must realise that you are a very powerful man at that polling station; more powerful than anybody else, than the commissioner of police, than Shagari if he comes there, than Awolowo, than anybody, than myself. You have the final say in that place. Therefore, in order to be able to do your thing, you must create an atmosphere of awe. For instance, when you get there, if you know that you want to act on this idea of dumping your ballot papers, you want to make sure that party agents don't disturb you and all the rest of that. As soon as you get there you say: 'Yes; I warn the party agents here. In fact, I am not going to take any nonsense today. FEDECO has spoken to us very sternly and I am not going to take any nonsense today.' And if you see that your polling clerk and your polling orderly are not going to cooperate with you, also tell them: 'You, sit down there for me and check names for me when I ask you to check. And you, sit down here. I will be sending you on errands any time I want, all right?' Then between you and the box, don't let anybody see what you are doing so that when you have any little moment you must start stamping. In fact, when you get to the counting centres, you can take your paper to one side and re-adjust."

He stopped and someone brought him the list of the people who should be there at this meeting. He then called the names on the list. There were two people more than the list said there should be but he did not mind. It showed how popular their cause was.

"So as I was saying, when you get to the counting centre as you did the last time, you can re-write your own proper record. Look, let me tell you, if you are still UPN, if you are UPN agents and you think you can help the UPN then let me remind you of what happened to the votes you gave to Awolowo last week, it is nonsensical. Whereas if you do what we want you to do, you can always come back to us and say: "Look, I contributed to your success, if I contribute to your success I deserve to be treated well.""

"Now to the question of payment. Until you have delivered. Last week was all simple, we didn't have time to talk, we didn't have time to perfect what you have to do today, but some people did well. This week, we have a specific thing and we are going to measure the return of each individual."

"Excuse me sir," someone shouted, "but something happened to me at our polling station. We had our men coming down to harrass us. Tell them to simmer down. It got to a stage I had to show my ID. I'm also for the party here. That was when he simmered down."

Then the NPN leader remembered what he ought to have told them earlier. "All right," he began, "let me tell you now how you will know our people will know you. Those of you who do not speak Yoruba I shall explain to you later. Now, when our people come, they will say *E ku ise o!* Normally, your answer should be a long *Ooh*. Instead, you should answer *Daadaa ni o*. Then he will say *Omo nko?* That's all. Let me repeat them:

E ku ise o!

Daadaa ni o

Omo nko?

Someone had a question. "Excuse me sir, within my own polling station, on my own, I made 50 ballot papers for NPN. So this time . . . what really happened was that had it not been the agent was hampering me I would have made more. He was difficult."

"That's all right," said the leader. "What happened last week is called in acting circles, 'dress rehearsal' - no matter how well you know your lines, how much you can do it well, it is on the first night that you will know whether you act well or not. Last Saturday was opening night, this coming Saturday is your second performance. You will do well. That's all for now. I have to go. Any other questions will be answered by the agents who are going to be briefed."

* * * * *

Sunday the 14th of August was a normal Sunday at 11 Methodist Church Road, Akure. Visitors to the house had begun to arrive as early as 5 am. The church next door had begun its usual Sunday service at about 6 am and it lasted the whole day.

"That is why I'm called the one whose house is next to God," Mr Fagbamigbe joked with his older brother who had come to see him, commenting on the earnestness of the Cherubim and Seraphim church next door. Down the street there was the usual dilapidated primary school typical of towns and villages in the southern parts of Nigeria. Since they too were going to church that Sunday morning the chidren were getting ready so they would not be late, all seven of them. But the older two teenagers, home on holidays from the universities of Ife and Ilorin, were not too keen on going to church and their parents did not insist. In the end, only the two parents went to the morning mass. Lunch was a feast and the whole family sat down to table and ate, joked and told stories which had nothing to do with the tense situation in town. No political colleagues called throughout the day, only family and friends. In the evening, husband and wife swopped stories about their first meeting and their decision to get married and how so many people had tried to come between them! And their children laughed. Even after the children had gone to their rooms to sleep, the two of them sat up talking and thinking aloud, sitting on the parapet upstairs, directly overlooking the street.

From an adjoining street, a Land Rover came roaring down towards their house, turned left and headed for the main road, but not before someone had shouted. "That's the house!"

"Did you hear that?" Mrs Fagbamigbe asked her husband.

"Hear what?"

"Someone said: *that's the house.*"

"It could have been any house," responded the husband.

She did not argue. She never argued with him: "I'm afraid."

"There's nothing to be afraid of!" he exclaimed and laughed heartily.

"All the same," she said, "I would feel better if we had some security guards around the house."

"Maybe I should call the police," he said and then went back to the general sitting room. He took the telephone and sat down on the long sofa. He called the commissioner of police. The answer from the other end was monosyllabic, laconic. Not enthusiastic. When he went to join her on the parapet she wanted to know what the commissioner of police had to say.

"He said he will send some policemen in the morning," he informed her. "What about tonight?" she asked. He did not answer. She stood up and went into her room without saying goodnight. He must have stayed there for another hour or so before dozing and waking up and hearing the night sounds of the town. Finally he went to bed and turned on the radio to listen to the BBC news as he usually did last thing before he went to sleep. The crackling sound of the radio was one of the sounds he woke up to the following morning at 5.30 am. There was a knock at the front gate of the house. It was his brother again. He went out and opened the door for him and together they sat down in the general sitting room. Their talk was desultory, without any particular direction, as if they were waiting for something to happen. At seven o'clock, they listened to the local news. The NPN candidate had been declared the winner of the gubernatorial elections in Ondo State against the anticipation of the people that the incumbent would be re-elected.

Immediately, the town of Akure roared into flames. The two-storey offices of FEDECO near the Oba's market were set on fire. The houses of prominent NPN politicians in the town were attacked and set on fire. They were still listening to the rest of the news when the thugs arrived at the house. There was general pandemonium along the street. The children were asked to leave the house and they slipped over the wall into the grounds of the C&S church and from there went to the houses of friends around. Meanwhile, car windows were being smashed and louvres destroyed. There was a new Peugeot 505 owned by an elderly teacher who had saved all his life towards this one single luxury and who had begun to park the car in Mr Fagbamigbe's compound for safety. The noise outside was unbearable.

"Let's get out of the house!" the wife cried to her husband.

"This is my house. I'm not leaving my house."

"A man cannot abandon his house," added his brother. "An Englishman's house is his castle!"

"Go," Mr Fagbamigbe said sharply to his wife, "and look after the children." She went to the front of the house and, using the staircase in front of the house, gained access to the street below. Then she dashed across to the house opposite theirs and stood by the window of their front room to watch what was going on. She could not say how many of them there were, but they seemed to flood the grounds of the house; they scrambled up the cement staircase at the back of the house, up to the rear of the house.

"She can't stay here," Mrs Fagbamigbe heard a woman's voice from behind her. "We will be in trouble if they know she is here." She turned from the window and ran to the back of the house from where she jumped into a little bush and here she waited.

"Do you have any money in the house?" one of the thugs asked Fagbamigbe. Maybe they would simply take the money and leave him alone.

"Yes," he answered.

"How much?"

"I don't know."

"Bring it."

He went into his bedroom and brought out a briefcase in which there was some 750 naira which he had received from some of the leaders of the NPN towards the election expenses. "Here it is."

They took the bag from him and poured out the contents. "Not enough."

"I don't have anything more."

"Come down!" they commanded. "And you too, Baba," they said to his elder brother.

"What do you want to do to me?" he asked as they brought him down to the parking area where the cars had been smashed up and the front wall had been pushed down. As he asked this question, someone from behind dealt him a machete cut between the collar-bone and the neck.

"God!" he screamed, and fell down. There was the motorcycle his brother had ridden to the house earlier in the morning. This was now lifted and placed on him with the petrol already leaking out. They then set the motorcycle on fire over his body and watched as he lay thrashing on the ground.

"Look for the wife!" shouted one of the thugs. "The children, and that Baba too!"

Two of the thugs went back to the house and threw some petrol on the roof and set it on fire. They came out on the other side of the house, crossed to the other side of the road, combing the bush around for Mrs Fagbamigbe. They caught her where she was hiding.

"Spray her!" shouted the one who seemed to be in command.

The other one poured what was left of the petrol in the jerrycan on her and threw the jerrycan at her. Her uplifted hands deflected the jerrycan.

"Light the matches!"

The second man struck the match stick against the match box and the match stick broke. He took another and the same thing happened.

"C'mon, what's the matter with you, you idiot?"

"Don't abuse me," protested the man who was trying to light the match. "Is it my fault if the matches would not light?"

"Maybe it's the woman's medicine that has got you!" the first man taunted his companion. The man who had been trying to light the match threw away the box of sodden matches and walked away from the kneeling woman. The other one followed him. Mrs Fagbamigbe got up and fled across the main road to the compound of the Catholic brothers and sisters of St Peter.

* * * * *

Dr Nnamdi Azikiwe, who had contested the presidential election for his parth the NPP, smarting from the humiliation of the brazen electoral fraud, issued a statement in which he declared: "I'm supremely confident that Almighty God will frustrate their knavery and ultimately expose their machinations and consign them to the scrap-heap of forgotten tyrants. History will continue to vindicate the just and God shall punish the wicked."

Chief Obafemi Awolowo didn't find it necessary this time to go to court. He told his party congress he would never seek elected office in Nigeria again and that democracy was dead in this country. Then he retreated to his country home refusing to comment further on public affairs. In November 1983, General Olusegun Obasanjo broke his silence to say that Shehu Shagari's mammoth cabinet of 35 ministers and seven advisers shows how light-headed Shagari was, given the delapidated state of the country's economy.

When invitation cards for Shagari's swearing-in ceremony arrived along with bullet-proof jackets, most Nigerians knew that something would soon give. Many of those invited did not turn up, fearing that shooting might take place during the ceremony. That ceremony went without a hitch. However, there was a feeling of foreboding about the possibilities of a coup.

Early in December, President Shehu Shagari returned from an overseas trip and made straight for Abuja. There, he met with his inspector-general of police and the service chiefs. By now, every important member of the NPN knew the thinking of their president. If there was going to be a coup d'etat, it would have to be their own senior officers that should be in power rather than the senior officers of the military who wanted a true change. This was the idea that Shagari now discussed with the service chiefs. They requested that they might be given time to think the proposal over.

That year, the Association of Nigerian Authors was meeting in Benin. The theme of their discourse was the commitment of the Nigerian writer to Nigeria. Many times many of the speakers were despondent as if the elections in the country had brought everyone to the end of their world. Mumman J

Vatsa, a general of the army was one of the writers who made presentations at the meeting. Vatsa had been writing poetry and encouraging the writing of poetry in the army since 1973 when Omibonoje publishers of Ibadan published his volume of poems on Nigeria's then twelve state capitals. He had declared in his presentation: "All of us, individually and collectively, must take a stand against the injustices and hardships of our present society." During the breaks, he took numerous photographs of the other writers for a book of photographs of Nigerian writers - Vatsa was also an amateur photographer.

"I'm off," he said as soon as he completed the photo-session.

"Where to?"

"Port Harcourt."

"What's happening in Port Harcourt?"

"Army Sports and I have to make presentations."

With that he got into the military Peugeot 504 saloon and with an outrider screaming in front of him, he rode out of the University of Benin and headed for Port Harcourt.

But it was not the Army Sports that was taking Mamman Vatsa to Port Harcourt. It merely provided a cover for him and some senior military officers both within and retired from the army. This was during the first week of December. At the end of the Army Sports the men went back to their stations to await what they had all agreed - to change the government.

Sam Ikoku, veteran of many political upheavals in the country, had a late dinner the last day of the year 1983. He and his wife then stayed up for the broadcast on television promised for midnight. That morning, there had been some martial music and then: "Fellow country men and women, I Brigadier Sanni Abacha of the Nigerian Army, address you this morning on behalf of the Nigerian Armed Forces. You are all witnesses to the grave economic predicament and uncertainty, which an inept and corrupt leadership has imposed on our beloved nation for the past four years . . ."

In subsequent broadcasts, he had asked Nigerians to look forward to a speech by the new head of state at midnight.

"I don't know what reasons they will give for the coup d'etat but some things are clear to me: there is some business about a Jaguar contract, there is Wushishi's retirement from the army and the fact that some people do not want Jega to be appointed as head of the army. There is also the fact that Shagari's second term had begun the trend of reducing the number of southerners in office and even to stop the possibility of someone from the south being the NPN presidential candidate come 1987. And the excesses of the chairman of the party and Umaru Dikko. Any others are raked up reasons after the fact." The whole nation stayed up by their TV sets. Waiting.

Twenty-two minutes into the year of George Orwell, a picture came on the screen of the Nigerian Television Authority. The voice of the picture intoned:

"In pursuance of the primary objectives of saving our great country from total collapse, I, Major-General Muhammadu Buhari . . ."

Sam Ikoku turned to his wife chuckling. His mind had already taken leave of the present. He said simply: "There is no coup. Let's go and sleep my dear."

(From *Just Before Dawn*, Spectrum Books, Ibadan, Nigeria)

Jackie Kay

ONE SEED 2

I can't believe something so simple
won't work for us

I can't believe the unwelcome
rush of blood every month

I can't believe I've tried for five years
for something that could take five minutes

I dread my blood like some women
dread bloodlessness

How can I want something so badly
and it not happen to me when

everybody else
is swelling up and walking the pram

buying cots and changing nappies
when all the talk is

When's it due you look flushed
is she teething?

I never liked bleeding anyway
now I hate it spiting our efforts every month

I'm so jealous of pregnant women
I cannot ask simple questions

Is it kicking
How long to go

I want to stand in front of my mirror
swollen bellied so swollen bellied

I want to lie on my back at night
I want to pee all the time

I crave discomfort like some women
crave chocolate or earth or liver

I'm hungry for imaginings
fingers forming hair growing

hungry for delivery
as some women fear it

I want the pain
the tearing searing pain

I want my waters to break
like Noah's flood

I want to push and push
and scream and scream

I want to watch the cord being cut
and let her suckle on my nipple

I can't believe something so simple
one sperm one ovum one night or morning

one calculated meeting
will not work to order

I can't conceive something so simple
won't work for me

THE VISIT

I thought I'd hid everything
that there wasnie wan give-away sign
left

I put Marx Engels Lenin (no Trotsky!)
in the airing cupboard - she'll no be
checking out the towels surely!

All the copies of the Daily Worker
I shoved under the sofa
the dove of peace I took down from the loo

A poster of Paul Robeson
saying give him his passport
I took down from the kitchen

I left a bust of Burns
my detective stories
and the Complete Works of Shelley

She comes at 11.30 exactly.
I pour her coffee
from my new Hungarian set

And foolishly pray she willnae
ask its origins - honestly!
This baby is going to my head.

She crosses her legs on the sofa
I fancy I hear the Daily Workers
rustle underneath her

Well she says you have an interesting home.
She sees my eyebrows rise
It's different she qualifies

Hell and I've spent all morning
trying to look ordinary
- a lovely home for the baby
She buttons her coat all smiles
I'm' thinking
I'm on the Home Run

But just as we get to the last post
her eye catches at the same time as mine
a red ribbon with twenty world peace badges

Clear as a hammer and sickle
on the wall
Oh she says are you against nuclear weapons?

To Hell with this. Baby or no baby.
Yes I says. Yes yes yes.
I'd like this baby to live in a nuclear-free environment

Oh her eyes light up.
I'm all for peace myself she says
and sits down for another cup of coffee.

AFTER MAMMY TOLD ME SHE WASNIE MY REAL MAMMY

I was scared to death she was gonnie melt
or something or mibbe disappear in the dead
of night and somebody would say she was a fairy
godmother. So the next morning I felt her skin
to check it wis flesh, but mibbe it was imitation
how could I tell if my mammy wis a dummy
with a voice spoken by someone else?
So I searches the whole house for clues
but I never found nothing. Anyhow after
I got my guinea pig and forgot all about it.

MY GRANDMOTHER

My grandmother is like a Scottish pine
Tall straight-backed proud and plentiful
A fine head of hair, greying now
Tied up in a loose bun
Her face is ploughed land
Her eyes shine rough as amethysts

She wears a plaid shawl
Of our clan with the zeal of an Amazon
She is one of those women
burnt in her croft rather than moved off the land
She comes from them, her snake's skin
She speaks Gaelic mostly, English only
When she has to, then it's blasphemy

My grandmother sits by the fire and swears
There'll be no Darkie baby in this house

My Grandmother is a Scottish pine
Tall straight-backed proud and plentiful
Her hair tied with pins in a ball of steel wool
Her face is tight as ice
And her eyes are amethysts.

JUVENILE DELINQUENT

I chase his Sambo Sambo all the way from the school gate.
A fistful of anorak - what did you call me? Say that again!
Sam - bo! He plays the word like a bouncing ball
But his eyes move fast as ping pong
I shove him up against the wall
Say that again you wee shite. Sambo Sambo, he's crying now.
I knee him in the balls. What was that?
My fist is steel; I punch and punch his gut
Sorry, I didn't hear you. His tears drip like wax.
Nothing he heaves, I didn't say nothing.
I let him go. He is a rat running. He turns
and shouts Dirty Darkie. I chase him again
Blonde hairs in my hand. Excuse me!
This teacher from primary seven stops us.
Names? I'll report you to the headmaster tomorrow.
But Miss! Save it for Mr Thompson she says

My teacher's face cracks into a thin smile
Her long nails scratch the note. Well well
I see you were fighting yesterday, again
In a few years time you'll be a juvenile delinquent
Do you know what that is? Look it up in the dictionary.
She spells each letter with slow pleasure.
Read it out to the class!
Thug. Vandal. Hooligan. Speak up! Have you lost your tongue?

Jackie Kay

Lotte Kramer

TWO POEMS AFTER RAINER MARIA RILKE

SONNET TO ORPHEUS IX

Only he, whose lyre was raised
even among shadows,
dare sing the unending praise
his sense barely knows.

Only he, who ate their meal
of poppy-seed with the dead,
will not lose the softest peal
of tone and thread.

If the pond's mirror often
for us may get blurred:
The image stays.

In the twofold sphere alone
shall voices be heard:
Mild and always.

AUTUMN DAY

Lord: it is time. The summer was so great.
Lay down your shadow on the sundial's face
and in the meadows let the winds run riot.

Command the last fruits' fullness in this time;
present them still with two more southern days
to urge them to perfection and to chase
the final sweetness into heavy wine.

Who has no house now, will not build his own.
Who is alone now, long will stay the same,
will sit up late, read, write long letters, roam
restlessly through tree-lined streets, again
walk back and forth when leaves ride in the storm.

DREAM YOKE

My shoulders ache
From the mud-weight of autumn,

My hair is shorn
By the edge of its rage,

My eyelids lose
The elastic of water,

My hands cannot rest
From the milk of its moon;

My legs are locked
In the granite of laughter,

I fall from the sun
To the round bruise of day,

I wake in my sheets
As a hamster of freedom.

ARRAN POEMS

1. TREKKING

On the way to the waterfall
We met a lost sheep
Fanfaring his aloneness
Through moss and bracken.
Somehow he had crossed
The unquiet river
Where boulders bridge
Their quarried path.
He looked at us with shocked eyes
And rushed into no-man's-land
As we stood helpless
Bog-weary in a dug-out of swamp.
Later we heard his cries again
Still hoarse in knolls of heather
Haunting us home.

2. RAIN

Rain initials this island
Inch by inch.
It signs each tree and flower,
Each pebble on the sea-hungry shore
Where yesterday's sun had bleached
A bench on the grass.
Today it sits there nameless and washed.
The hills are smudges
Whispering under grey wool,
Hardly alive.
A blue boat ducks
Under the relentless signature.

3. LAMLASH BAY OPPOSITE HOLY ISLE

To let this bay caress you in your veins,
To be a central island set in light,
To look across the misted hills where sight
Is interrupted by the rocks, to let
The sea collect your every thought and breath:
You would be homeless here at home at last,
You would be nameless in this island's name.

4. THE TIDE

Every time
The bay is bandaged
By the sea
Covering wounded rocks,
Sand and grass.
Like big sores
They reveal themselves
When the tide goes out.
Then we walk
In lanes of lesions
Picking our way
Through healing answers.

Lotte Kramer

Illustration to 'The Tide' by Kirsten Harris

The Poetry of Robin Williamson

Charles Stephens

Robin Williamson grew up in Edinburgh; during the early 1970s he lived at Innerleithen, in the Borders. Innerleithen was once surrounded by the ancient wood of Caledon, a vast domain of mistletoe-garlanded oaks, hawthorns, apple, beech and birch trees which stretched, in prehistoric times, from Galloway in the west to Newcastle in the east, up to the boundaries of Arthur's seat in the north and then beyond into the further reaches of Perthshire. 'Caledon' may have meant 'the place of the young Goddess' and it is more than likely that the historical Merlin, who was a councillor and bard to a king based in Carlisle, fled into the Wood of Caledon after the defeat of his master in a seventh century battle referred to in the *Goddodin*. This Merlin would have spent his last days in the wood of Caledon, in mental disarray, straitened circumstances and political exile. It is possible, if one bears in mind the nature of the surviving poetry of his contemporary Taliesin, that Merlin's attested stature as a poet may have given him access to shamanic initiation practices and wisdom. If this were so, then it is also conceivable that this Merlin, a formidable antagonist of Christianity by consequence of such wisdom and initiation, was lured to his death by the missionary St Kentigern at Drumelzier, where, some tales tell, his body yet lies. Williamson has often visited Drumelzier.

It was in this same land that Thomas of Erceldoune, whose 'Sir Tristram' has a claim to being considered the first poem written in Scots, met, according to the words of the ballad, the Queen of the Faeries one May morn under the Eildon Tree. Some, including Sir Walter Scott, have said that the wizard Michael Scot split the Eildon Hill into three and lived in a stone tower on the edge of St Mary's Loch.

The strange, poetic stories of Merlin, Thomas the Rhymer, Michael Scot and the enchanted forest of Caledon, which was not unlike that of Broceliande, are familiar features of Border myth and legend. They reached a much wider audience as a result of Sir Walter Scott's collections of the Border Ballads and his own poems and novels. James Hogg's 'Kilmeny' and the story that his grandfather was the last man to 'see the faeries dancing' provide a fascinating nineteenth century reprise of the legend of Thomas the Rhymer. The atmosphere and detail of these tales can also be found in the poems and stories of Stevenson and Buchan (whose contribution in this respect has been seriously underrated. The splendid 'Witch Wood' which Canongate reissued in 1987 is only one example of Buchan's marvellous handling of Border material) and in many modern retellings. As it happened, I learned of this lore from the poetry and songs of Robin Williamson. I have always considered him to be, before anything else, a Border poet in the long line which reaches back, via Buchan, Stevenson, Hogg and Scott, to Thomas the Rhymer, Taliesin of Carlisle and even to his fabled predecessor Merlin himself. The magical legends and poetic stories of the Borders have been implicit in Williamson's work from the beginning:

In a schoolboy's hands that cupped that water
Merlin of the Borders turned in his river grave
where Powsail Burn meets the Tweed
the wild bees hummed
a brown bull grazing in the meads
a seeming peace, a soft summer's day
where I first read, and reading, saw the paper dissolve away.
(Five Denials on Merlin's Grave, 1979)

The presence of the Borders and its folklore can also be felt in the lyrics of the Incredible String Band albums 'Wee Tam' and 'The Big Huge' (1968): "Pining for the pine woods/ that ached for the sail . . ." ('The Half-Remarkable Question') "Misty Mountains where the eagles fly/ lonely valleys where the lost ones cry . . ." ('Ducks on a Pond'); "Mad as the moon when Merlin falls . . ." ('Ducks on a Pond');

Safe and secure in the skirts of the midsummer wood
cooking soup with stale words and fresh meanings it tastes so good
The green wolf with his bunch of red roses is slinking away
all on a summer's day. ('Lordly Nightshade')

A long wind a weaving mind
over all the land the wild flowers grow,
echoing kind to kind. ('The Iron Stone')

The story of the Incredible String Band rightly belongs to that of 1960s pop music and the folk revival. However, there were, at the heart of that extraordinary phenomenon, a number of themes which have, in the unfolding of Williamson's subsequent activities as a poet, some importance for poetry in Scotland and Britain as a whole. In the first place, as has been suggested, the great tradition of the Border ballads, with their fertile poetic legends, was the basis of Williamson's own poetry and imagination. Secondly, from the days of the Incredible String Band, Williamson has exhibited a confidence in the power of poetry which is unusual in the twentieth century. The example of Burns has always been important to him. Williamson looks to the poetry of Burns as an achievement to be aspired to and tested by, not just, as MacDiarmid once said of something else, 'charmed onto the mantlepiece and left there'. Apart from MacDiarmid, the only other (English-language) British poet of recent times to have pursued a genuine aspiration to 'bardic' status was Dylan Thomas. Williamson prefaces his song 'For Mr Thomas' on his 1981 'Songs of Love and Parting' album as follows: "I first heard 'Under Milk Wood' on BBC radio when I was nine. I was lying in the dark. War surplus earphones of a crystal set had my head in a vice-like grip." The song goes on:

With all the usual ceremonial you were crowned one night
King of the field where the doctors nail the cows
to make the cock's quill the right of language
and the pricking heart a sword against the hours.

Let smirking scholars writhe in their favoured bondage
to hold you plaintiff to the charge of art

Exhibit A: he fails on legendary lines
singing mother I want a bullet in the heart

the judge in me sucks eggs and jerks the sacred meat
for the boy in me still dreams in Milk Wood town.
Like two provincial bastards playing the galleries
I hold your photo to the mirror upside down . . .

Staged up like Falstaff or the wild welsh Rimbaud
You'd laugh to see the monochromes they make of you . . .

Let us watch while the days grow daily more mundane
that rough god go striding with the shears
hack wide the bellies of swollen mountains
and rip molten heroes forth to their furious stars.

These days, in contemporary English poetry, one never finds that
raunchy, vital confidence in poetry which was demonstrated in the lives and
work of Thomas and MacDiarmid. Such vitality is rarer than it was in
Scottish poetry, but is still to be found here and there, in particular in
Williamson's writings and songs. So it is a disappointing fact of life that
Williamson is not ranked as a poet in Scotland at present. His work is not
found anywhere in the plethora of recent anthologies of contemporary
Scottish poetry. There is something perverse about this. In my opinion, the
best of Williamson's work will eventually find its place beside that of
MacDiarmid, Sorley MacLean and Hamish Henderson. Happily, times may be
changing. Hamish Henderson's underpublished poetry will soon be available
in a proper edition. Alan Jackson, a contemporary of Williamson's, with
whom he shares many qualities, has recently published *Salutations: Selected
Poetry 1962-89* (Polygon 1989)

Not the least of Williamson's efforts is his prose poem 'Edinburgh'
(1983). This 'tour-de-force' deserves to be placed alongside the many fine
satires which 'Auld Reekie' has inspired from the pens of Dunbar, Fergusson,
Garioch and Goodsir Smith. Some extracts might convey its ribald flavour:

Auld Reekie, Auld Reekie, not so reekie now, maybe, but you're just as
sneaky, as cockieleekie, draggletail dreepy, drammy, persnickety,
ba'faced old besom of a ministerial town. Squatting there between the
Pentlands and the Firth like a puddock on a cabbage leaf. A
fisherman's walk you are, three steps and overboard. And not a step
but fashes the dead and stirs up evil stoors, dour legalities, withered
posies, lost loyalties, unforseen reverencies, magic trickeries, branded
candelabras and beautiful, guiltless mirrorings of time and time and
time again.

Your girlish face unkissed. For the heart confuses hearts with
gates, and gates with gaols, and gaols with God. And the canny hand
lets go the wee glass and drops a button in the collection plate with a
clink just like a threepenny.

I've lived all over this town in single ends by the score. I've slept
upon a thousand floors, weel, a sight more than ten. Most of them are
torn down now by courtesy of the Godalmighty University. Take
Society Buildings for instance, once a good doss . . . now there's a

patch of green grass and a patch of benches there . . . Oh everything's built and rebuilt continually, that's philosophy for you.

Williamson's poetry has also been inspired by those ideas and powers of which Robert Graves wrote so eloquently in 'The White Goddess' (1948). In the notes to *Five Denials on Merlin's Grave* (1979), a poem much involved with such matters, Williamson writes:

"One looks at a tree, a woman, a stag, a man and sees only a tree, a woman, a stag, a man and not what they mean . . . In the old Welsh 'Red Book of Hergest' there is found this saying: "Three things that enrich a poet/ Myths, poetic power, and a store of ancient verse". And what is this poetic power? It seems to me that it is related to the comprehension of words, and to the understanding of human symbols, and to the language in which the sea talks to itself, together with an impassioned purpose of communication. But to begin the poet must know himself. Why a store of ancient verse? To know what has been said is to know what was worth saying once, and to obtain an understanding of what must be said next. Also, ancient verse in those days would tend to mean history. Why myth? It is a language that dreams are made on.

Williamson sheds further light on these matters in the preface to his poem 'The Song of Mabon' (1983):

Mabon son of Modron is a very ancient Celtic stag-horned deity, spirit of the year's second half. Apollo-like patron of the arts as I conceive him, though some regard him purely as a hunter god, lord of the animals, or as he who pursues the souls of the dead. Basically Mabon has a solar association and shares in common with other horned deities attributes such as the ancestor of the race etc. He is a form of the Mediterranean Orion who pursued the Seven Sisters till he and they were turned into constellations, and of Nimrod, mentioned in the Bible in connection with the building of the Tower of Babel. The building materials of the Tower of Babel are equated in Celtic lore with the various parts of speech, and the Tower is regarded as a poetic metaphor . . . Snowdrops, the first flower of spring, are called in Welsh, 'Cloch Mabon', Mabon's bells, or baby's bells, 'mab' basically meaning boy or hero, originally. Hence, 'Mabinogi' means lad's story or hero tale. Mabon, son of Modron, meaning something like Great Son of Great Mother. Some scholars consider a lost story of Mabon to have been originally an underlying story of the other stories of the cycle . . . Mabon is said to have been stolen from between his Mother and the wall when only three nights old, and finding him involved in a variety of quests and magical animals, each older than the last, a blackbird, a stag, an eagle and finally a salmon, who directed them to the prison where Mabon was confined.

For Williamson, the mythical figure of Mabon is that of the poet who is imprisoned in time and history and whose task is to recover his freedom. The poet's quest is also a metaphor for that of humanity as a whole. The

Green Man of folk tradition is another image of such a poet:

> The Green Man becomes to me increasingly symbolic of the
> archetypal artist for whom the answer is always blowing in the wind,
> who quests for his own nature, hounding through the darkness, and
> paints in his dancing life from the colours of black (which contains all
> colours) the visible light of a real and future dawn invisible to the
> hounds, and who is ever hounded himself by the Mother of the Gods,
> his own imagination. (*Five Denials on Merlin's Grave*, p22)

Sentiments such as these are familiar enough from the writings of Robert
Graves. However, unlike Graves, who never, in my opinion, managed to rise
above his Georgian origins, Williamson has succeeded in bringing light and
power into the rhythms and imagery of his poetry. These extracts from 'The
Song of Mabon' (1983), reveal the gulf which separates the poetry of
Williamson, to whom the mythology is real and true, from that of Graves, to
whom it was a literary conceit and polemical posture. Willliamson is writing
of the mystery of poetry, about what Graves called the 'White Goddess':

> A story to be told when journeys are broken
> by fall of night or by first light of day
> a secret to be spoken when turnings are taken
>
> by spring's first flower or by the first shower of snow
> a song to be whispered to ears that will listen
> for love of the red rose
> for love of the white rose
>
> it is of the royal road
> by May Day and midwinter and summer's end
> it is of the boundaries of the world
> and of the other world
> it is of the choice made when no choice is given
> and of the weight of the horned mask on the face
> by the gallows, the cradle and the bridal feast
> I trace now my own features in the stone . . .
>
> I sing the alchemy of the dead and the unborn
> I sing the dark origins of the rising year . . .
>
> and a voice buried in my heart is crying
> I am the risk and purchase of the world
> carry me with you   ('The Song of Mabon')

In 1983, Williamson wrote a text for Moving Being's adaptation of *The
Mabinogion*. This gave him the opportunity to deal directly with mythic
material and to re-express it in a contemporary idiom. A number of
twentieth-century poets (David Jones, Charles Williams, John Heath-
Stubbs, J R R Tolkien, Robert Graves for instance) have attempted, on the
whole unconvincingly, to handle this kind of material. Williamson, as he had
demonstrated in lyrics such as 'My Name is Death', 'The Eyes of Fate',
'Waltz of the New Moon', 'Three is a Green Crown', 'Maya', 'Lordly
Nightshade', 'The Iron Stone' and 'The Circle is Unbroken' which he wrote
for the Incredible String Band in 1966-68, could handle difficult mythic

material with a light and very beautiful touch. His lyrics for *The Mabinogion* reveal a mastery of this idiom:

It is of our hearts the legend's pulse
their agony our foe
homely and strange among river names
and the names of towns
and garlanded with roadside flowers
the figures stalk and dance
and die like flames.   ('Naming Pryderi')

Legend and wild horses, hard to bind
of heroes or gods once honoured
callers of the wind and the cattle of the sea
or human as we and born to die.

Let it remain poet's gospel
lost words and hidden music
a shy child through fingers peeps
and a hidden story between the lines.   ('Cradlesong')

Williamson's finest long poem, to date, is *Five Denials on Merlin's Grave* (1979). This poem blends together autobiography, history, mythology and sharp satire. Although the form is free, the poem is bound together by a marvellous rhythmical music and considerable verbal virtuosity. Like MacDiarmid, who could attain a potent musicality in a work like *The Drunk Man Looks at the Thistle*, Williamson is a poet who can 'sing':

worshipping across the world a music
that nests in bird's song, insinuates in river babble,
sings in the soft south wind and burns in the burning flame.

To lay a burden and a tune that shall catch the heart and descant yet
to the echo of that oldest song of all, that stirs the bold.

Williamson is reminding us of those values for which poetry once stood and for which it rarely stands today. Those values could be called, sententiously, the 'bardic' tradition, but they are in fact much more familiar to us than that vague, portentous notion. Williamson's poetry may or may not relate to 'bardic' traditions, Ossianic or otherwise, but he is making a poetry that would have been understood by MacDiarmid, Stevenson, Byron, Shelley, Scott, Hogg, Burns, Fergusson, Shakespeare, Spenser, Dunbar, Henryson and Thomas the Rhymer. He is bringing to life a poetry which, as he says himself towards the end of *Five Denials on Merlin's Grave*:

makes a lie of history
whose presence hints in every human word

(which) somehow reared and loosed an impossible beauty enduring yet
among the green islands of the grey north sea
and I will not forget.

Williamson's *Five Denials on Merlin's Grave* are affirmations of the potency of poetry, and the celebration of human love is a theme which beats in the very heart of poetry. It is no accident that Chaucer, Henryson, Dunbar, Sidney, Spenser and Shakespeare - the founders of the tradition of

148

Scots and English poetry - should also have been supreme poets of love. MacDiarmid, MacLean, Henderson and Jackson, with whom I have associated Williamson in this article, are also fine exponents of this tradition. Also like singer-songwriters of the 60s and 70s such as Bob Dylan, Leonard Cohen and Joni Mitchell, Williamson is also a notable love poet. Williamson's Incredible String Band lyrics of the years 1966-68 acted as an informal accompaniment, or even serenade, to many affairs and passions during the 'summer of love' and the years which followed. There cannot have been many poets of that period, besides the aforementioned singer-songwriters and maybe the Beatles, of whom this was true. These examples of Williamson's love songs may convey some idea of their quality:

> Let night enfold, let silence own
> the kiss you spare for me alone.
> Time has awhile that none can bind.
> Tomorrow thieves your hand from mine.
>
> Then lean to me, darling, darling, darling,
> your dear dark head my heart above.
>
> The summer's night that turns the tide
> yields this to those whom lives divide.
> Love has a right that none can bind.
> Tomorrow thieves your hand from mine.
>
> Then lean to me, darling, darling, darling
> your dear dark head my heart above.
>
> ('Sigil' from *Songs of Love and Parting*, 1981)

> She who my heart loves
> lives far away from here
> and it is my yearning for her
> that has made me pale.
>
> I chose in a choice of beauties
> a maiden of pureness
> but before she will be mine
> fire will freeze over.
>
> Riches are worthless,
> beauty will not endure,
> but love is sure as steel
> when two hearts are true.

('Tra Bo Dau' (When Two Hearts are True), *Music for the Mabinogi*, 1983)

. As Shakespeare once put it, music is the food of love, and also of poetry. Williamson, an accomplished musician, is also a gifted lyric poet. His poetry, like that of all genuine lyric poets, has a 'singing line'. It also touches on the realms of myth, prophecy and vision, as did Taliesin and Merlin of old and MacDiarmid and MacLean in our own day. In these very traditional ways, Williamson has claims to be a noteworthy poet. His work over the past quarter of a century is evidence that the long poetic tradition of the Borders is an old song which is not yet ended.

Charles Stephens

John Agard

GIVE THE BALL TO THE POET
(For Angus Calder)

People often ask me
what I'd like to be
if I wasn't a poet.
I not so sure dey had
in mind a fast bowler.

But yes, I fancy meself rubbing
a poem on mih flannel
till de poem red as hell,
and if de poet
supposed to commune with nature,
de fast bowler (don't forget)
does talk to de wind.

Is alright when words sing
in lyrical flight,
but when dey also have grit
and double bite
de literary boys call it
ambiguity of meaning.
I rather call it deceptive swing
of a Michael Holding.

Watch dat West Indian poet bowling
with unpredictable run-up.
No daffodil or buttercup.
Is strictly hurricane whispering
in a six-ball sonnet.
Now and then drop one short
like a flick-of-the-wrist haiku,
bounce a home-truth or two
and force a politician to make a stroke.

You might think I aiming joke
at the literary establishment,
if I say poetry is de motion
of three wrecked stumps
re-collected in tranquillity.
But is no laughing matter
when a poet feeling on de boundary,
and a crowd hungry for blood
start to shout
GIVE THE BALL TO THE POET
GIVE THE BALL TO THE POET.

CHECKING OUT ME HISTORY

Dem tell me
Dem tell me
Wha dem want fo tell me

Bandage up me eye with me own history
Blind me to me own identity

Dem tell me bout 1066 and all dat
Dem tell me bout Dick Whittington and he cat
But Toussaint L'Ouverture
no dem never tell me bout dat

Toussaint
a slave
with vision
lick back
Napoleon
battalion
and first Black
Republican born
Toussaint de thorn
to de French
Toussaint de beacon
of de Haitian Revolution

Dem tell me bout de man who discover de balloon
and de cow who jump over de moon

Dem tell me bout de dish run away with de spoon
but dem never tell me bout Nanny de maroon

Nanny
see-far woman
of mountain dream
fire-woman struggle
hopeful stream
to freedom river

Dem tell me bout Lord Nelson and Waterloo
but dem never tell me bout Shaka de great Zulu
Dem tell me bout Columbus and 1492
but what happen to de Caribs and de Arawaks too

Dem tell me bout Florence Nightingale and she lamp
and how Robin Hood used to camp
Dem tell me bout old King Cole was a merry ole soul
but dem never tell me bout Mary Secole

From Jamaica
she travel far
to the Crimean War
she volunteer to go
and even when de British dais no
she still brave the Russian snow
a healing star
among the wounded
a yellow sunrise
to the dying

Dem tell me
Dem tell me what dem want to tell me
But now I checking out me own history
I carving out me identity.

John Agard

aonghas macneacail

oideachadh ceart

do john agard is jack mapanje

nuair a bha mi òg
cha b'eachdraidh ach cuimhne

nuair a thainig am bàillidh, air each
air na mnathan a tilleadh anuas
as na buailtean len eallaichean frainich
sa gheàrr e na ròpan on guailnean
a sgaoileadh nan eallach gu làr,
a dìteadh nam mnà, gun tug iad gun chead
an luibhe dhan iarradh e sgrios,
ach gum biodh na mnathan
ga ghearradh 's ga ghiùlain gu dachaidh,
connlach stàile, gu tàmh nam bó
(is gun deachdadh e màl as)

cha b'eachdraidh ach cuimhne
long nan daoine
seòladh amach
tromh cheathach sgeòil
mu éiginn morair
mu chruaidhchas morair
mun cùram dhan tuathan,

mu shaibhreas a fheitheamh
ceann thall na slighe,
long nan daoine
seòladh amach
sgioba de chnuimheagan acrach
paisgte na clàir,
cha b'eachdraidh ach fathunn

cha b'eachdraidh ach cuimhne
la na dìle, chaidh loids a chaiptein
a sguabadh dhan tràigh
nuair a phòs sruthan rà is chonain
gun tochar a ghabhail
ach dàidh an sgalag
a dh'fhan "dìleas dha mhaighstir"
agus cuirp nan linn as a chladh

cha b'eachdraidh ach cuimhne
an latha bhaist ciorstaidh am baillidh
le mùn a poit a thug i bhon chùlaist
dhan choinneamh am bràighe nan crait
gun bhraon a dhòrtadh

cha b'eachdraidh ach cuimhne
an latha sheas gaisgich a bhaile
bruach abhainn a ghlinne
an aghaidh feachd ghruamach an t-siorraidh
a thàinig air mhàrsail, sa thill gun ordag a bhogadh,
le sanasan fuadach nan dùirn

cha b'eachdraidh ach gràmar
rob donn
uilleam ros
donnchadh bàn
mac a mhaighstir

cha b'eachdraidh ach cuimhne
màiri mhór, màiri mhór
a dìtidhean ceòlar
cha b'eachdraidh ach cuimhne
na h-òrain a sheinn i
dha muinntir an cruaidhchas
dha muinntir an dùbhlan

agus, nuair a bha mi òg
ged a bha chuimhne fhathast
fo thùghadh snigheach,
bha sgliat nan dearbhadh

fo fhasgadh sgliat
agus amuigh
bha gaoth a glaothaich
eachdraidh nam chuimhne
eachdraidh nam chuimhne

a proper schooling

for john agard and jack mapanje

when i was young
it wasn't history but memory

when the factor, on horseback, came
on the women's descent from
the moorland grazings laden with bracken
he cut the rope from their shoulders
spreading their loads to the ground,
alleging they took without permit
a weed he'd eliminate
were it not that women
cut it and carried it home
for bedding to ease their cows' hard rest;
and there was rent in that weed

it wasn't history but memory
the emigrant ships
sailing out
through a fog of stories
of landlords' anguish
of landlords' distress
their concern for their tenants,
the riches waiting
beyond the voyage,
the emigrant ships
sailing out
a crew of starved maggots
wrapped in their timbers,
it wasn't history but rumour

it wasn't history but memory
the day of the flood, the captain's lodge
was swept to the shore
when the streams of rha and conon married
taking no dowry
but david the servant
who stayed "true to his Master"
and the corpses of centuries from the cemetery

it wasn't history but memory
the day kirsty baptised the factor
with piss from a pot she took from the backroom
to the meeting up in the brae of the croft
not spilling a single drop

it wasn't history but memory
the day the township's warriors stood
on the banks of the glen river
confronting the sheriff's surly troops
who marched that far, then returned without dipping a toe,
clutching their wads of eviction orders

it wasn't history but grammar
rob donn
william ross
duncan ban
alexander macdonald

it wasn't history but memory
great mary macpherson
her melodic indictments,
it wasn't history but memory
the anthems she sang
for her people distressed
for her people defiant

and when i was young,
though memory remained
under a leaking thatch,
the schoolroom slate
had slates for shelter
and outside
a wind was crying
history in my memories
history in my memories

                              aonghas macneacail

THE · SCOTTISH · CLASSICS

SPARTACUS

James Leslie Mitchell
'Lewis Grassic Gibbon'

Number 14 in the *Scottish Classics* series brings back into print the first modern edition of this major work of Scottish fiction, based on the author's own text. Ian Campbell, editor, offers a description of Gibbon and his work and a brief evaluation of *Spartacus* as historical fiction.

p/b   *272pp*   £6.75   *0 7073 0545 4*

For further information on the *Scottish Classics*, please contact:

SCOTTISH ACADEMIC PRESS
139 Leith Walk, Edinburgh EH6 8NS

Est. 1945

Non Profit Making

TRACE YOUR SCOTTISH FAMILY TREE

Please send for details to:

Scots Ancestry Research Society
3 Albany Street
Edinburgh EH1 3PY
Telephone 031 556 4220

Painting the Darkened Canopy

A Critical Survey of Contemporary Irish Poetry Publications

Hayden Murphy

Irishness is not primarily a question of birth or blood or language; it is the combination of being involved in the Irish situation, and usually of being mauled by it. (Conor Cruise O'Brien)

The flaw in this judgement lies in its avoidance of the restoring quality of language in a shared literature. In this article I deal with comparatively unknown English language writers, but my criticism also applies to work from writers in Gaelic such as Tomás Mac Siomoin, Seán Hutton, Micheál Ó Siadhail and Nuala Ní Dhomhnaill.

At the end of my reading I found that a pessimism which disheartened me to passive silence during the dreary Seventies and acquisitive Eighties had muted the optimism necessary to hear emerging voices from a remarkably resilient Ireland. For I am not blind to the realities facing a new generation of Irish writers: in parallel to Dr O'Brien (b. 1917) I place a recent observation by the Belfast-born poet Gerald Dawe (b. 1952) -

> The central fact in recent Irish history has been the eruption and continuation of political upheaval (in the North) matched by deep-seated social tension and resentment in the Republic. Life changed irrevocably both directly and indirectly for hundreds of thousands, including my own generation, who inherited ordinary hopes in the future only to see them break up in the grim squalor of daily bombings and nightly assassinations. (*Graph*: No. 6, Summer 1989)

The Poet, unlike the Doctor, does not step back in mock horror and abdicate, he continues to insist, in the same piece:

> As discriminations are being forced daily upon people in the language they use and share political discourse in; 'freedom', 'pro-life', 'unity', 'independence', 'minority'; so the language of poetry needs similar scrutiny. it is the poets themselves who must initiate and acknowledge the obligation since they *produce* meaning, significance, reality, call it what you will, through and in language. Often it seems, however, that poets avert their imaginations from *language-slump* and, in so doing, minimalise the important challenges facing their work as poets today.

I (b. 1945) recognise this demand to absorb, assimilate and articulate can produce dry-as-dust didacticism, but I concur with its generalised, and acceptable, plea for a more truthful expression of personal impressions. With cautious, optimistic curiosity I approach the work of a number of writers who have emerged over the past twenty years.

In Dublin at least three publishing houses specialise in new material. In no order of critical preference I start with Raven Arts Press (PO Box 1430, Finglas, Dublin 11). Founded in the late 70s by poet, novelist and playwright Dermot Bolger, Raven issues about ten new titles a year, mainly poetry, though its intention is to concentrate on fiction, drama and pamphlets.

Dubliner Bolger (b. 1959) recently received the Hennessy Award for his contribution to Irish literature. His latest novel, *The Journey Home* (1990) strips Dublin of literary glamour and repopulates the city with the derelicts of everyday reality; earlier novels *Night Shift* and *The Woman's Daughter* received several prizes. His play *The Lament for Arthur Cleary* was a critical success at last year's Dublin Theatre Festival. Repossessing the past is the haunting purpose of his new collection *Leinster Street Ghosts*. The title poem is dedicated to Harry Sheridan, a real 'Dub', and "a fierce man to talk". However, it is the more sombre tone of another poem, 'Not The Stream Of The Infants', that gave fright to my earlier opinion that Bolger was trapped in a rhetoric of self-conscious urban complications. Here, the ghosts share their discomfort with discomfited humans:

> You think I have been banished
> Behind a plate-glass cul de sac,
> But this night, while you consume
> The speckled eggs of capsules
> To hasten the rush of morning
> Not only your fridges are murmuring.

The insomniac's familiar whispers are heard. In other poems his derelicts are given dignity, and the 'haunted acres' are re-populated.

A Raven poet, new to me, is Dubliner Sara Berkley (b.1967). She has spent some time in the USA and has two collections in print. *Penn*, her earlier work, has a beguiling air of discovery, like finding a voice. Betrayals litter the pages. "Driving storms is fun until they crash". "Sister America" is left behind. Towards the end the author is thinking "of women who have roses above their doors,/ And weep into their aprons". *Home Movie Nights* lead to better things. Now landscapes are invaded rather than wardrobes rearranged. Surreal voyages are embarked on, "ghost notes make the memory tremble". "You scorched me slightly", says the cyclist author of "Just Don't Walk Out in Front of my Bike". But she survives. At times, loose structured lines become monotonous without the discipline of metre. Then the writer and reader "connects with a bright shock". The end of love, "the fretted moan", frazzles. Her biting observation "your lies have piranha teeth" reminds me of a younger Leland Bardwell. This "truth-gatherer" seems to have had an overdose of lies. A contempt of deceits, human and animal, spit out of the later poems. One wishes to soothe, to wish gentleness back, gratefully I heard optimism in the final poem 'The Courage Gatherer'.

It is good to see my old friend, Desmond O'Grady (b.1935), a much travelled man, back in Kinsale and writing. Rich textured experience make his poems minefields where events fuse the explosive ideas to create sulphurous firework displays, always dangerous to the man connecting the elements. *Alexandrian Notebook* has the author "humming alone in foreign places" watching blue-habited nuns moving in cloisters like "two fishing boats sail side by side in the bay". Another cup of black coffee and the poet is sounding "grace-notes of giddy aspiration". Then there are the exiled moments, when words lodge a saddening warning against the lonely hours when writing is sole solace, the empty page the remaining guest. Desmond, onetime secretary to Ezra Pound, film extraordinary for Fellini, Roman in

Cairo, Palestinian in Dublin, destructive carpenter in London's Irish Club, reader and lover, across the now short distance I simply say 'Ma-Salaam'.

Another acquaintance is Bryan Lynch (b. 1945), though we have slipped apart on 'uncarpeted' areas of politics since his adventurous days in the Sixties when he sank an inheritance into the publication *The Holy Door* (1965-67). The most attractive aspect of *Voices From The Nettle Patch* is the green fading to aquamarine cover by the poet's wife Rosaleen Davey. This is a deliberately eclectic collection. The wit and presumed wisdom about the poet's contemporaries in Dublin looks smug on the page. The ironies that I know from previous collections become repeated platitudes now sounding pompous. As he writes in "Child of Memory": "My memory reproduces/ small things." Like the journalist John Feeney, whom he talks of as "a harmless poor devil" and "a decent skin", Lynch is now mummified by the cultivated meanness that pervades these pages. It was not always so. Sadly, he is too influenced by, and not really removed from, the current archness of Mr Charles Haughey's cultural foghorn Anthony Cronin. Pity. When they wish to be, Lynch and Cronin are rewarding poets.

It is a pleasure to turn to Sabastian Barry's *Fanny Hawke Goes To The Mainland Forever*. Another Dubliner, Barry (b. 1955) is also a novelist and playwright. His novel *The Engine of Owl Light* (1988) received respected praise. The poems are inhabited by the forlorn, the poor, travellers, passengers away from roots, immigrants, including "a poor respectful friend/ of gentling Catullus" This is a travelogue of the dispossessed over centuries, migrants escaping from their decaying familiars. In the centre is a twenty-part series entitled "Kelsha Yard, 1959". Rotting vegetables counterpoint lives rotating between cradle and grave. In abandoned houses lies "Summer's conscience on the sills". There are few homes. In "Gipsy Camp, 1944" events in Europe invade the more commonplace mortuaries of otherworlds. Fanny Hawke of the title is an 'outlaw' Quaker marrying into Catholic Cork. The poet's own antecedents (his mother is actress Joan O'Hara, his father the architect and poet Frank Barry) are the hidden archaeologists beneath a narrative that is marvellously satisfying and richly mysterious.

Cork-born Aidan Murphy (1952) has also published two earlier collections, *The Restless Factor* (1985) and *The Way The Money Goes* (1987). *Small Sky, Big Change* deals with the emptiness of solicitous religion in the lives of those ruled by "Methylated Physics". It is a harsh "welcome to Vaudeville" where the writer is guised as a "prying neglected fish in this imperfect climate". The claim "I at last am where I belong" is in sad brittle fashion placed where "in the silence you can hear/ the dogmas bicker".

The best thing about Tom Lonergan's first collection is its title, *The Sound of Umbrellas at Work*. Much of the writing is conceit disguised in lower-case mock self-regard. The pieces are spinning balls in the air belonging to a juggler who has decided to keep his hands in his pockets. They are lazily constructed and indifferent in content. A piece entitled 'View from a Bedroom' verbally romps an "urgency of thighs" with a "torrent of saliva tasting of soil, of ashes". It is embedded in my mind as an argument for celibacy. No style, all stylistics.

Another Dublin-based publishing firm is Dedalus (24 The Heath, Cypress

Downs, Dublin 6), directed by the poet John F Deane. Born on Achill Island, Co. Mayo in 1943, Deane retired in 1979 from teaching and founded Poetry Ireland, a centre of information on poetry publications and readings. In the mid-8os he started Dedalus. He publishes ten titles a year.

His new book, his third, *Road, With Cypress and Star* is complemented with "textual illustrations" by the Dublin sculptor and artist John Behan. The title poem juxtaposes a Van Gogh landscape with life on Achill. A commitment to Christianity fills the pages. A secular-spirituality is present in several prose-poems that seem austere, but on further reading have an enviable serenity. This seems to be a new departure for this writer. I am curious, if apprehensive, about the direction this work is leading. I hope 'gentleness' will ward off smothering veneration. There is so much sensitive, instinctive and instructive 'goodness' in this writer that a selfish reader like myself dreads the approach of monastic silence.

Deane is co-translator with Uffe Harder (b. 1930) of *The World As If*. This is a selection from ten collections over the last thirty years, in Danish, by the latter. From the early "listening for the snap of branches in the wood", to caustic comments on the translucency of clouds at which "you can't help laughing", there is a melodic affinity to European surrealism earlier this century. Both poets' humanist sympathies seep into all the poems. As Deane writes in his introduction, "Here are the commonplace, the strewn components of living, set up and redeemed by poetry."

With respect to all the authors with Dedalus, the most interesting addition to its list is Thomas Kinsella (b. 1929). *One Fond Embrace* is number 13 in a series of Peppercanister poems, written since 1972, and previously published under the author's imprint with numbers 8-12 appearing as *Blood and Family* (OUP) in 1988. Kinsella, comparatively unknown outside Ireland is, since the death of Beckett, Ireland's major figure in European literature.

Over the past twenty years his work has unfolded into a veritable saga. Bloody Sunday, the 10th anniversary of Kennedy's assassination, the death of the composer Sean O'Riada have provided identifiable incidents in his unravelling of a peculiar imploding personal universe centred in a quiet area of Dublin beside a canal already commemorated by Patrick Kavanagh (1905-67). Kinsella's harsh judgements on contemporary politics and environmental issues give his work a philosophical unity that is far from comforting. In a non-sequential way he is over-tracing the ambitions of a clear-sighted child determined from innocence to "see and get to know everything".

The poems in the new book shuffle personal memories to illuminate these philosophical and historical preoccupations. Speculators and politicians are pilloried. He resignedly declaims: "The persons and circumstances in this poem are real, but their parts have been redistributed so as to make them unrecognisable. "Like the characters of Beckett his 'implants' are valid, even when false. They are humanely stripped of artifice. Vulnerable, but curiously safe, encased by the poet's sympathy: "Fellow citizens! I embrace/ Your grasping manners, your natural behaviour/ As we thrive together for an instant." He views us with the benign, desolate fondness of Dean Swift. These poems are literary mnemonics "more spleen/than good sense" of our troubled past and present. Kinsella has, like Swift, "read the ground". The knowledge he is accumulating, and the wisdom he is sharing, provides us with significant illumination of our tattered times.

Yet another Dubliner is Macdara Woods (b. 1942), poet and co-editor of the magazine *Cyphers*. *Stopping The Lights in Ranalagh* is his third collection. Again, the emphasis is on the poetic disciplines, the control of line and feeling, the accurate listening to his own heart-metre:

> You knew I could not step into your anguished eyes
> Without some fitting song or symbol to explain
>
> Why I have such dependence upon such ruin of rhyme.
> Could I reduce complexity and tell it to you plain.

Here is an unusual depth of craft and compassion. The poet's assimilated reading includes Rilke, Dylan Thomas, Bob Dylan, John Berryman, Yeats, but more unusually in these days of grim solemnity he has the confidence to edge along the lampposts with the wry Don Marquis. "Frankly Mr Fly/ it is a damned nonsense for food to stand up on its hind/ legs and say it should not be eaten." Lunch follows. Macdara Woods, observant waiter at the table, serves. But there is an inherent gentleness in his laid-back observations. His poems, after years of hard apprenticeship, supplement the early verve and pulse-feel for language. They are rich and stimulating. I hear, as I read, the poet's voice in performance. He does not recite, he celebrates.

Another Dubliner is Valentin Iremonger (b. 1918). Over the years he has been Irish Ambassador in Sweden, Norway, Finland, India and Portugal. He won the AE Award for new writers in 1945. His translations of Brendan Behan's Gaelic poems are definitive. His new collection, *Sandymount, Dublin* was, I suspect, intended to appear under the Dolmen Press imprint of the late Liam Miller. All credit to John Deane for picking up such collections that might otherwise have been delayed or lost. These poems are smooth: love poems, poems of conscience, poems of "The Caring Day". A marvellously realistic evocation of a hangover in "The Gull" melodically throbs with misery. There is a beautiful technique apparent, maybe too transparent, in the eloquent "Poem in the Depths of Summer", for his wife:

> Summer flickers down, I know; but my darling, we
>   Have something on tap
> To tide us from year to year: a reserve of love
>   Deep and free:
>   And, through winter, perhaps,
> Invest us, here we have sustinence, over and above
> Our possible needs - till like trees we blossom
> Again, our lives' leaves tossing.

The detached tone of his version of 'King Sweeney's Valediction', merits comparison with Seamus Heaney's recent treatment of the same theme.

Hugh Maxton's new book defies definition. A hint at the roots of *The Puzzle Tree Ascendant* lies in the apparently haphazard lines and shapes of Mary Fitzgerald's 'Geometric Progressions' that accompany the text. They, with the prose and verse, recall recently-elevated ghosts; composer Freddy

May, artist Cecil King, architect/writer Niall Montgomery. Yet they are not elegies. They are places where Maxton punctuates a life-precis. As he writes, elliptically, around an episode in Yugoslavia: "desolation stood around, admonished". Maxton, like poet Brian Coffee, is an 'experimental classicist", sombrely re-arranging his sardonic "arrangement of our damnation".

Bill McCormack (b. 1947) adopted the name Hugh Maxton from the obvious Scottish sources early in his career, to identify his poetic work. He has also written informatively and lucidly on Irish literary matters. An essay in a recent issue of *Krino* on Heaney's prose, and in particular his preoccupation with Central European writers ('The Holy Sinner') I recommend to all interested in contemporary criticism. His own creative work enlarges perception. As his final, more formal verse "Nature Morte" concludes: "here is light/ In need painting the darkened canopy"

Unfortunately these words form a sad link to conleth Ellis's final collection *Darkness Blossoming*. He died in 1988. These poems were written during and after visits to Africa in the 80s. The jacket note gets it right: these are poems "inspired and unified" by "the unglazed lands that take/ their colours from the potter's stage" His "potter" is his creator. He identifies his muse as "a person's profound need for regard". Over the years I have read with pleasure his work in Irish (Gaelic) and English. In his absence there is now an untimely silence.

Waterford-born Padraig J Daly (1943) is an Augustinian priest in central Dublin. *Poems: Selected and New* are gathered from three earlier collections *Nowhere But In Praise* (1978), *This Day's Importance* (1981) and *A Celibate Affair* (1984), together with fourteen new poems. Jack Harte, founder of the Irish Writer's Union, speaks in his brief introduction of becoming "acquainted with the man and his work ten years ago" and having "understandable misgivings at the prospect of a priest singing the praises of life". He learnt otherwise. Years ago, without knowing Padraig was a priest, I was fascinated by the simple clarity, allied with formal sophistication, that marked his poems. That was 1971. For eight years he generously contributed poems to Broadsheet. I was always, in my atheistic fashion, 'sanctified' by his modest delight at having readers. Re-reading his poems brought that contagious pleasure back to me.

Despite the emphasis so far on publishing in Dublin, the most startling change in the past decade has been literary activity outwith the city, most notably in Galway. Typified by a wall mosaic in a monstrous Cathedral depicting crucified Christ flanked by Patrick Pearse and John F Kennedy, Galway was religiously philistine in my youth. In the late Seventies this changed. To outsiders, the Druid Theatre Company was the most visible sign of movement. Then Gerald Dawe moved to the area and introduced a weekly "Writing in the West" page to the local *Connacht Tribune*. Writers from outside the area were invited to contribute, new poems solicited and published, writing was encouraged. Now an annual Arts Festival supplements the traditional "Galway Races" and complements the Oyster Festival. Dawe, when not lecturing in TCD Dublin, edits the invigorating literary magazine *Kriño* from the area. New tunes and words are being celebrated.

In the town - well, alright, the "City of the Tribes" - Jessie Lendennie edits the admirable magazine *The Salmon* and is also Director/Editor of Salmon Publishing (Auburn, Upper Fairhill, Galway). In the absence of biographical information, and from a brief phone call, I can only guess at her American provenance. No matter, even if she is from "over there", it is the neighbouring parish of Aran, and her writers show a healthy disdain for a "provincial" label. With four to six titles a year she has produced books which show "original spark" and are "intelligent and innovative".

She is also an accompised writer. In her prose-poem 'Daughter', the central character Emma lives a childhood where "the air smelled of heat and ice". She hears in an enveloping California, trees, maternal exhort-ations, sea-sounds, and the reassuring rustle of familiar clothing. Dreams conjure up brilliancy. Daylight is a sombre disappointment. She shudders at the memory of receiving a "dying parakeet" won at a fair stall by a drunken father. Then cancer attacks her mother and she "began to hate the sun". In this beautifully-presented book, the dying fall comes when the departing daughter remembers the child crying "If you love me, take me with you."

Under the Salmon imprint I was delighted to read Ciaran O'Driscoll's first book *Gog and Magog*. O'Driscoll (b. 1943) is editor of the *Limerick Poetry Broadsheet*. In an important review of Paul Muldoon's *Meeting the British* (Cyphers, No 30) he writes of the northern poet's vacillation: "In terms of *comment* (he) seems to implicate art in a conspiracy to gloss over reality with pleasing illusion." O'Driscoll's own work is sensible of suspected dilettantism, is the work of one who has survived London, knowing that "city's penny-pinched long finger". He has an alter ego, Hogan, who "insists on diagnosing the World's ills". Within his "unpublished corpus" are "chunks of soul/ evinced with the aid of batons". In the title poem the violence of the century comes to wrath in an occupied part of an ancient land where Gog and Magog were powers in the mind; only a "shout's echo" to today, when:

> a dead postman caught in a crossfire
> cycling round a street corner
> spoke of two men
> with identical weapons
> who stood over his body
> and traded greetings curtly.

O'Driscoll concluded his commentary on Muldoon by finding "too much raw material, too little shape". In his own work I discovered "the country of conversations" that can still capture all the tenderness of familiarity. It is there in his poem 'Roads' (for his daughter?)

> Where is the road to Wigan Pier
> which I have tramped on all my days
> inspired by Larkin, Connolly?
> This road leads downwards, to the sea;
> and at the pier my boat delays.
> But there remains a child so dear.

Material shaped from rawness. He has just published his second collection *The Poet And His Shadow* (Dedalus). The search for light continues. It is full of tender and wry observations. Promise has developed into potential lyricism. O'Driscoll is an intrepid explorer of the minute, which with craft and confidence he gives universal importance.

Rita Ann Higgin's *Witch in the Bushes* explores the horrors of domestic strife, and exposes the poverty of emotional penury. Short lines about taut situations meander through the pages. Secret lovers "burgle glances". Some poems lay too much emphasis on eloquent spaces. Line rhythms can fail to move the mind with the eye. The author should be cautious about half-delivered pronouncements - regurgitated they can sound disastrously glib. Her two collections are published in one volume, *Goddess and Witch*.

American Ann Kennedy's *Buck Mountain Poems* is a slender volume, lovingly produced with attractive illustrations by Allison Judd. It deals with the writer's retreat from urban distractions to a sanctuary in nature in "the landscape of Scriabin". Her musically-orientated musings did not work for me. That book, and Paul Genega's *Striking Water*, are both "financially assisted" by a New York publisher (Vivien Leone, Lioness Books). Genega's reminiscences of an American Catholic childhood are unlike anything I have read outside the pages of James T Farrell. The young boy going to his first confession "convinced we had committed communism somehow" becomes the accoustically acute adult who hears the moan of his "Mourning" as "An Electric Sea/ in a black shell. A sustained identification with the vulnerable permeates the later poems. I am anxious to read more.

However, the strength of Ms Lendennie's list lies in her selected women writers. Limerick-born Clairr O'Connor (b. 1951) in *When You Need Them* records creation "from the Belly", through the protected years of childhood when impulses live in "another place", to the artistry of adult anxiety when "waves and voices" clamour to be recorded. Individual poems evoke memories of Ann Sexton, but these are not derivatives; they are interesting, evolving, articulate articles of faith in survival. I do not share the author's admiration for Irina Ratusinkaya's translated work, but as I read this first collection I hear again the determination to conquer isolation that fused the Russian writer in public performance in Scotland several years ago. O'Connor's observations, as she chops up "fibrillous tangles" and fights against encroaching "terror" are definite articles. This is poetry declaring its priorities, proclaiming itself urgent to be read, important to be remembered.

Jo Slade (b. 1952): her *In Fields I Hear Them Sing* also has this urgency to communicate that I find overwhelmingly welcome at a time when much poetry in English is sedate or safely dry. Her individual gift is to involve her reader. I read "If they ask me to find yesterday/ I will say I gave it/ To a woman crossing a bridge" and think this writer would be good company on a zebra crossing, anywhere. In the title poem "two strong mountain women" who "could tell of bad times/ coming 'cause no sight was made/ of small swallows" educate the girl to dream of them, and hear them singing. They instill in her strength and understanding that becomes ingrained compassion. Only my admiration for the writing in this first collection makes me appeal to the author that in future she resists the temptation to overload with brief 'squibs' the odd pages between the many poems.

Finally I come to the work of the editor of *Writing in the West*, Eva Bourke, born in West Germany. *Litany for the Pig* (illustrated by Jay Murphy) is her second collection. In the opening poem she identifies the enemy: "Two middle-aged Euro piranhas/ in silver hair and red ties/ have made a huge kill today/ Eyes dim like headlights." She then retreats to re-emerge and gleam again in poems of place. She is in Clare, I suspect the Beckett boneyard of the Burren, where "The stone never quite cools off here/ where it has colonised the peninsula". But even these precisely-trapped areas in the mind had not prepared me for the magically evoked tone-poem to her music-mad father. 'Moments Musicaux' is both for and about him. His ability to transform into a "living language" a narrow escape from Nazi Germany, an uneasy exile in the orange glades of Haifa, and a homesick return to Austria, is the substance of his story. Spiritually he is perpetually allowing "the dead bury the dead" and permanently playing "Bach, Mozart, Chopin/ And above all, Schubert". He is memorable. So is his daughter's memorial. If other poems fade it is only that the revelations within this poem are connecting and concentrating at the time of writing. These are moments to savour; they are a pleasure to share. I hope the writer is getting the recognition she deserves.

There are other publishers and publications I would like to return to in more depth in the future. Blackstaff Press (3 Galway Park, Dundonald, Belfast BT16 0AN) publish important reprints, such as the Irish novels of Joyce Cary *Castle Corner* (1938) and *A House of Children* (1941). They also have a growing list of new fiction including the prize-winning *Ripley Bogle* by Robert McLiam Wilson and the impressive novels of Michael P Harding, *Priest* (1986) and *The Trouble With Sarah Gullion* (1988). Paul Durcan, Padraic Fiacc and Robert Johnstone are among their poets and they are also responsible for the influential *The Younger Irish Poets* (Ed. Gerald Dawe). Field Day (Orchard Gallery, Orchard Street, Derry) are issuing a sequence of pamphlets that are signposts, rather than footnotes, on Irish political, social and literary issues. In Waterford, Edward Power with Riverine (Garter Lane Art Centre, 5 O'Connell St, Waterford) is foraging new territory and Peter Fallon continues to produce his all-important Gallery Press (19 Oaktown Road, Dublin 14). An invaluable guide to these and other outlets comes again from the industrious Ms Lendennie in Galway and I recommend her *Salmon Guide to Poetry Publishing in Ireland*.

I am sure there are omissions in my listings but at the end of this general survey I would like to return to an important pivotal point in the second half of this century. This was the short-lived 'small' magazine *Arena* (1963-1965) edited by Liam O'Connor, Michael Hartnett and James Liddy (bound and re-printed by the Malton Press, Monread Road, Naas, Co Wicklow, 1981). Arena took its title from Rilke's *Die Tauben*:

> Back in dovecote, there's another bird,
> by all odds the most beautiful
> one that never flew out, and can know nothing of gentleness
> Still, only by suffering the rat-race in the arena
> can the heart learn to beat.

Inside an oxygen tent a heart beat is heard again, and from the outside of that tent I am, to use Hugh Maxton's phrase, prepared to paint that darkened canvas with loud praising colours. Maybe the birds will nest in this new arena.

Hayden Murphy

Nuala Ní Dhomhnaill

BÉALOIDEAS

I

Sínim siar sa bhfeileastraim breá árd
atá ag fás anseo in aice is duimhche Fionntrá
lá breá gréine
is cuimhním ar an bhfear a cuireadh sall
go ceartain na Cluaise fadó ag an saor bád
ag triall ar mhalairt tháirní.
D'imigh sé leis sa tsiúl ab fhearr
a bhí aige go dtí an áit seo. Ansan do shín sé siar,
d'fhéach ar an ngréin is dhein sraic mhaith codlata
dó féin. Dhúisigh is d'eirigh aniar is d' fheach
ar an ngrein is thuig sé ná féadfadh sé bheith tagaithe
aniar ó Bhaile Móir san méid sin aimsire. Do shín
sé siar arís is dhein an tarna sraic thar n-ais
is nuair a dhúisigh sé bhí an ghrian ag dul i léig.
Do bhailibh sé chuige a chuid táirní isteach i gceirt
is b'eo leis thar n-ais gan stad go saor an bháid
nár aithnigh cioca.

II

Nó an bhean a bhí ag dul 'an tsáipéil
chun a coisreacan taréis linbh.
Nigh sí a cosa i dTobar Mholaga
is chuaigh an tobar i ndisc.
Chaith an sagart teacht is paidir a rá
trí huaire ós a chionn is é a choisreacan
sar a dtiocfadh an t-uisce thar n-ais.
Nó an ceathrar fear a thug naomhóg leo
ar a ndrom ón nDúinín go Loch Corráilí
chun dul i ndiaidh an phlanda sin go dtugann siad
an duilleóg bháite air. Thugadar sceana feamnaí
is maidí rámha leo chun é a bhaint
is sa deireadh d'árdaíodar leo ualach maith den ruibh.
Fuaireadar oiread san callshaoth ag teacht abhaile leis
nár deineadh é níos mó is tá an loch triomaithe anois.

III

Tá scata seanduine cois na tine i mbothán
a caint ar so is ar súd,
is ag tabhairt scéalta don mbailitheoir.
"Ó", arsa fear acu, "na mná a bhí anso fadó
bhí ceol ionntu". "Is ní haon tae a bhí á ól acu",
is choirce, póire is meacain bhána is iasc is báirnigh".

"Bhí bean i gCill Uraidh, i bparóiste Fionntrá
a thug ocht gcliabh déag iascán aníos as Faill
na Béirdri ar a drom is do shiúlaigh abhaile tráthnona.
Saolaíodh cúpla di an oiche chéanna".

"Ba mhaith ann í".

"B'fhiú bia a thabhairt di".

Tugaim faoi ndeara
ná hiarrann éinne acu ar mhair an cúpla.

AN BÁD SÍ

Triúr a chonaic is triúr ná faca
na fearaibh ar na maidí rámha,
seaicéidí gorma orthu agus caipíní dearga,
ag dul isteach go Faill na Mná.

Sinne a bhí ag piocadh duilisc
ar na clocha sa Chuaisín, -
mise is Neil is Nóra Ní Bhrosnacháin
a chonaic iad, is triúr eile ní fhaca rian.

Bhí ár gceannaibh síos go talamh
ag piocadh linn is ár n-áprúin lán.
Mise is túisce a d'ardaigh m'amharc
nuair a chualamair fuaim na maidí rámha.

Ní fhéadfainn a rá an cúigear nó seisear
fear a bhí istigh sa bhád.
Bhí duine acu thiar ina dheireadh á stiúiriú
is gan aon chor as ach oiread leis an mbás.

Do liús is do bhéiceas féachaint
isteach faoin bhfaill cár ghaibh an bád.
Chonaic triúr iad is ní fhaca an triúr eile
in áit chomh cúng ná raghadh ach rón.

Is dá mbeidíst ag straeineáil ann go maidin
go brách na breithe ní fheiceadh rian
den mbád úd nárbh aon bhád saolta
a chonac le mo dhá shúil chinn.

Dúirt na seandaoine nár mhithid
teacht abhaile is an Choróin ar á
mar gur minic a bhí a leithéid cheana
á thaibhsiú do dhaoine ar an mbá.

Triúr a chonaic is triúr ná faca
na fearaibh ar na maidí rámha,
seaicéidí gorma orthu is caipíní dearga
ag dul isteach go Faill na Mná.

Nuala Ní Dhomhnaill

FOLKLORE

I

I stretch out in the beautiful high shellister that grow here near the sand-dunes of Fintray, on a lovely sunny day, and I remember the man who was sent over to the smithy of Cluas long ago, by the boatmaker, in search of different nails. Off he went at the best pace he could muster till he reached this very spot. Then he stretched out, took a look at the sun and saw that he wouldn't make the journey back from Balmore in that amount of time. He stretched out again and had another long nap and when he awoke the sun was getting low. he gathered the nails he had into a rag-cloth, and back he went without a stop to the boatmaker, who didn't notice any different.

II

And also the woman who was going to chapel for her purification blessing after giving birth. She washed her feet in Molaga's well, and the well went dry. The priest had to come and say a prayer over it three times and bless it, before the water would return.

Or the four men who carried a curragh on their backs from Dooneen to Loch Corralee in search of that plant they call the drowned leaf (the water-lily). They brought with them seaweed-knives and oars to cut it away, and in the end lifted a good load of the vegetation. They had such trouble coming home with it, that it was never repeated, and now the loch has dried up.

III

A crowd of old folk are by the fire in a bothy talking about this and that and giving tales to the collector.

"Oh," says one of the men, "the women that were here in days long past, they had music in them".

"And it was never tea they were drinking," said another man, "but goat's milk, and wheatbread and oatbread, seed potatoes and parsnips and fish and limpets".

"There was a woman in Killury, in Fintray parish, who carried eighteen baskets of mussels up from Faill na Béirdri on her back and who walked home in the evening. That very night she gave birth to twins".

"She was good to have around".

"She was worth feeding".

I notice that not one of them asks if the twins lived.

THE FAIRY BOAT

Three who saw and three who didn't see the men plying the oars, with their blue jackets and red caps, going in to Faill na Mná (the Woman's Cliff).

We who were picking dulse on the stones of the Cuaisín (the Little Cove) - me and Nell and Nóra Ní Bhrosnacháin we saw them, and three others saw nothing.

Our heads were bent down to the ground as we picked away with our aprons full. It was me who first raised my gaze when we heard the sound of the oars.

I couldn't say if it was five or six men who were in the boat. One of them was in the stern, steering it, as motionless as Death itself.

I shouted and yelled trying to make out, in below the cliff, where the boat had gone. Three saw them and the other three didn't, in a spot so narrow that only a seal would venture there.

And had they peered there till morning, till Kingdom Come they would have seen not a trace of that boat which was no earthly boat that I saw with my own two eyes.

The old folk said it would be best to come home and recite the Rosary as often before had such a thing been revealed to people as a presage of death.

Three who saw and three who didn't see the men plying the oars, with their blue jackets and red caps, going in to the Woman's Cliff.

Nuala Ní Dhomnaill
Translated by M.Byrne and Brian Courtney

Eunice de Souza

Colin Nicholson

When the Scottish Poetry Library first opened in 1984, among those present was the Indian poet Eunice de Souza. She has visited Scotland several times since, and was one of the participants at the Commonwealth Writers' Conference which Edinburgh hosted in 1986. Her poems have appeared in *Chapman*, and as part of their Spring list for 1990, Polygon has brought out a collection of her work, *Ways of Belonging: Selected Poems*. Her writing is characterised by an astringent wit, and when she reads her Indian material of an often satirical kind it is delivered crystallised and edged by an impeccably English accent.

She was born in 1940 in the old British station of Poona, now called Poone, in the state of Maharashtra on India's west coast. At that time still under British control, Poona was a colonial summer resort during the last years of the Raj. In this ambience de Souza went to school and grew up. Born a Roman Catholic, after a long struggle to free herself from the Church institutionally, she remains one 'nominally'. She went on to study at the University of Bombay and after postgraduate work in the United States she taught in Darjeeling at the University of North Bengal, went to England for a couple of years, and took up her present post as lecturer in English Literature at St Xavier's College, Bombay, in 1969.

Considering herself "in a general sort of way" a Christian, her poetry is marked by an oppositional stance to much of what the Church has promoted, and a direct and unadorned presentation of her perceptions. I wondered what was the inspiration for this crafted illusion of artlessness:

"I remember, when I began to think about writing, I was attracted to the medieval Hindu verse of the Bhakti poets. They were reacting against the whole Sanskrit tradition, and in a peculiar sense I think I saw it as a form of Protestantism. These poets were all from lower castes who were not allowed access to the Vedas, so in a way their work could be looked at as a kind of Reformation. They were not breaking away from the idea of God but from the Brahmin stranglehold on it. I read a lot of their stuff in translation, and one of the earliest poets I read was Tukaram, who wrote in Maharati. I liked these short poems addressed directly to God, with their speaking voice, very easy on the page":

> Tuka, forgive my familiarity.
> I have loved your pithy verses
> ever since that French priest
> everyone thought mad
> recited them, and told us
> of his journey with your people.

"What I want is not only that conversational tone, but also the sense of unfinished communication. I want there to be a sense of something left behind, so that the conversation can be taken up again at some other point.

With me, re-working often means making a poem shorter: I've often cut the last line because I want that deliberately jagged effect at the end of some of my poems. 'Forgive me, Mother', for example, ends:

> I was never young.
> Now I'm old, alone.
>
> In dreams
> I hack you.

In the original version I finished with 'flesh from bone', but that rhyme with 'alone', quite apart from being redundant, seemed to be softening the effect, so I cut it out and left the poem with that stronger final line."

A recurrent imagery of cutting suggests at times a self-lacerating aspect to some of these poems, but de Souza can also introduce softer ironies into her reflections upon the influences of religion, beginning with her schooldays when she was taught by Irish nuns. 'Sweet Sixteen' ends:

> Phoebe asked me:
> Can it happen when you're in a dance hall
> I mean, you know what,
> getting *preggers* and all that, *when*
> you're dancing?
> I, sixteen, assured her
> you could.

But where did the name de Souza come from? "We were all Hindus, converted by the Portuguese in the sixteenth century. We didn't intermarry. There is a separate community who did intermarry, called the Anglo-Indians: yet the term used to describe us is Mestiz, which means mixed. It was part of Portuguese policy to alienate us as much as possible from our backgrounds, so we were given Portuguese surnames, often the name of whoever was converting us. Many Hindus allowed themselves to be converted, mainly, I think, to save their skins, since the Portuguese were very vicious about their conversion policy. So there has always been this feeling that we were different, and superior to Hindus, which is something I explore in my early poems. But in fact our social structure is very similar to that of the Hindus. We still have the caste system, we always preserved that. Sometimes a village is divided into caste-sections, and sometimes entire villages are identified as belonging to a particular caste. So, for example, if someone wanted to check me out, he might ask which village I was from, or which part of the village. This would be an attempt to identify my caste and hence my social status."

These social and religious divisions and stratifications create different kinds of separating ignorance, sometimes to comic effect:

> My Portuguese-bred aunt
> picked up a clay Shivalingam
> one day and said:
> Is this an ashtray?
> No, said the salesman,
> this is our god.

First published in the *Times* of India, this poem created something of a storm, revealing the sensitivities and censoriousness religion invokes. Letters from the South accused her of insulting millions of Hindus and asked what would be the Christian reaction to the suggestion of a crucifix being used as a fork. The poem's point about misunderstanding between communities was lost. But such confined views characterise her own community too.

"Certainly the idea of marrying a Hindu, a Moslem or whatever would be considered to be something absolutely horrendous. This is not history because it's still happening to younger cousins of mine." Her poem 'Marriages are Made' takes a jaundiced view of these arrangements:

> The formalities
> have been completed:
> her family history examined
> for TB and madness
> her father declared solvent
> her eyes examined for squints
> her teeth for cavities
> her stools for the possible
> non-Brahmin worm.

In Southern India there are still churches where Brahmins will not receive communion at the same altar-rail as lower castes, and the poem 'Varca, 1942' offers one historical instance of this, recording an Archbishop's attempt to democratise the structure locally, by insisting that landlords and peasants worship together. De Souza was intrigued that a religion basically feudal in structure itself should countenance such a move. The landlords resisted violently and the poem concludes:

> After many months
> the Archbishop relented
> and the landlords repented
> and everyone worshipped together
>
> And the landlords were landlords
> and the peasants peasants
> ever after.

So forms of alienation in this verse spring from a variety of causes. In contemporary India considerable heat and dust is generated by hostility to poets writing in English as opposed to one of the native languages.

> My students think it funny
> that Daruwallas and de Souzas
> should write poetry.
> Poetry is faery lands forlorn.
> Women writers Miss Austen.
> Only foreign men air their crotches.

"Very often people say 'why do you choose to write in English?' You don't choose. English is my only language. My maternal grandmother didn't speak English, though she understood it, so we often spoke Konkani with her, which is the language of the West coast, Goa and that area. My mother grew up speaking Konkani, and learned English at school. But I grew up speaking English. I don't think alienation is a matter of language, though I'm constantly being told I'm alienated. I'm even told I'm not Indian. There are people who want to make me feel alien because I am some kind of Christian, and therefore in a minority. Then I write in English. Then I am a woman writing in English. But when I wrote these poems which are about Catholics, I was writing them as poems about my community, and what it felt like growing up in that community. I discovered looking back at the book (*Fix*, published in 1979) that many of them are sympathetic to women. So a lot of people picked that up and consider me to be a feminist poet, which in a sense I am."

These themes come together in a poem like 'Catholic Mother', which focusses upon an insensitive father until the impact of its final two lines:

> By the Grace of God he says
> we've had seven children
> (in seven years)
> We're One Big Happy Family
> God Always Provides
> India will Suffer for
> her Wicked Ways
> (these Hindu buggers got no ethics)
>
> Pillar of the Church
> says the parish priest
> Lovely Catholic Family
> says Mother Superior
>
> the pillar's wife
> says nothing.

Deploying a sometimes scornful irony, several poems satirise this kind of Catholic middle-class hypocrisy in India.

"The tone comes, at times, from a really deep outrage. Even at school I was outraged by Catholic ideas about birth control, and growing up in such a claustrophobic community, I felt anger against such restrictive attitudes and ingrained habits of mind. In my poem 'Bandra Christian Party', I try to express a sense of the frustration that can arise from living in such a community, from having to put up with such limited ideas of what personality might be, what it could and should mean:

> What personality says Dominic
> such pink lips men and
> look at that chest
> so comic says Mabel
> keeps the crowd going
> says Hetty
> Fred is the life of the party.
> Come on men Fred give us
> a song calls Mabel
> What personality says Dominic
> such pink lips and look
> at that chest.

But pressures on women, and women writers in India, contribute to an anguish in this writing, and de Souza conveys a sense of suffering more effective for its apparent simplicity. Confronted by male writers who look down on personal elements in poetry, and proclaim instead the desirability of writing on large historical or mythic themes, 'Transcend Self You Say' responds:

> Friend, the histories I know aren't fit to print.
> Remember Padma, widowed at seventeen,
> Forbidden to see the sun for a year,
> allowed out to crap only at night
> when the pure are out of the way?
>
> The perfect book is
> one long cry in the dark.

That cry recurs, but I was interested in the image of the widowed Padma.

"This is literally true. Widows were just locked in a room until everyone was out of the way, and couldn't be contaminated by their presence. It's a Hindu thing. I mean, the best thing for widows is to burn themselves; isn't that what is happening now! If you are a widow, it's obviously your fault that your husband died. It's nothing to do with him: he died because there is something wrong with you. Therefore a widow is a sign of bad luck, evil and so on."

Perhaps inevitably for a writer in her position, a search for roots forms one aspect of the writing, but no easy resolutions are offered:

> I find the caretaker dead
> the white ants burrowing
> grand-aunt clothed in cobwebs . . .
>
> I hear the pigs forage
> and know this is not home.

"My family originated in Goa. So what do I find when I go back to Goa? I find everything crumbling. And what is not crumbling is new and vulgar."

There is, too, a range of sympathy, from the portrait of the Anglo-Indian 'Miss Louise' fading into old age and living on memories of youth, to reformed whores in Bombay:

> Sarla Devi, Kusum Bala, Rani Devi,
> all of ill fame.
> I read your story in the morning paper:
> you refuse to wear ankle-bells
> worn for generations . . .
>
> Sitting alone alone in a Bombay restaurant,
> listening to the innuendoes of college clerks
> and a loose-lipped Spanish priest,
> I know something of how you feel.

"These are all women trying to give up being prostitutes, symbolised by the ankle-bells of the dancing girls. They are women trying to emerge out of their earlier circumstances - more histories not to be spoken - as I am."

Colin Nicholson

Miroslav Holub

GREAT FOREFATHERS

At night
their silhouettes are outlined
against the empty sky
like a regiment of Trojan horses.
Their whispering rises from wells
of evidently living water.

But when
day breaks as an egg cracks,
and on the instant men armed with truncheons are born
and mothers bleed,

they appear as butterflies with wings
of cabbage leaves,
as jelly from fog,
in fading infantile outline,

their scarcely suggested
hands shake,

they forget to breathe
and are afraid to speak a single
intelligible word.

All in all,
we have inherited more genes from the viruses
than from them.

They have no strength.
And we ought to be the strength of those
who have no strength.
Trans: Jarmila & Ian Milner

ABOUT A POEM

It is
          a fuse,
you light
somewhere in the grass,
or in a cave
or in a third-rate
                              saloon.

The little flame races
among the blades,
among the startled butterflies,

among terrified stones, among sleepy tankards,
racing,

growing a little or vanishing
like pain in a supernumerary finger,
hissing, spluttering,
halting
       in microscopic vertigo,

but right at the end
             it explodes,
a boom as from a cannon,
tatters of words fly through the universe,
the day's walls reverberate,

but even if
no rock is burst
someone will say at least-
          Hell, something's happened!
                      Trans: Ewald Osers
           (First published in *Prospice 16* in 1985)

SUCCESSFUL YOUNG MAN IN THE LABYRINTH

When he got past the eighth turn
he cleared his throat and yelled:
Minotaur, why not be sensible? Here's
my hand, you show me the way out
and I'll guarantee you twenty of the prettiest girls.
Sure thing, Minotaur.

I replied, unseen:
And are you aware there are
demons?
      Come off it,
he replied, don't be silly. Here's
my hand, I know where you can make a pile.
We'll go fifty-fifty, okay, how about it?
I'm a reasonable person,
be reasonable too, Minotaur!

And I replied:
And are you aware that reasonableness
is only a milder form
of feeble-mindedness?
          Go to hell,
he yelled, won't you understand that it pays off
to get on with people? Getting on with people
pays off, our sergeant used to say

when he dusted our huts
with bedbug powder, so stop putting on airs!
I'd say in this dump you'll barely keep body and soul together.

I replied unseen:
Can't you see that you're sitting
on the point of a needle that's darning
the threadbare trousers of your history?
And what, in point of fact, is your aim,
boy?

          Well, that's just it,
he said. My aim . . . I'd say it is
to be back home. Be in clover.
        And I'd make a copy of this labyrinth,
        might come in handy, if you know what I mean . . .

So I gave him to the demons,
made them chuck him out of the labyrinth.
And had the passages dusted
with that powder.

No doubt he lived for a great many years
and distinguished himself at the
dog races.

                    Miroslav Holub
              Trans: Ewald Osers

Shirley Geok-lin Lim

AH MAH

Grandmother Lim was smaller
than me at eight. Had she
been child forever?

Helpless, hopeless, chin sharp
as a knuckle, fan face
hardly half-opened, not a scrap

of fat anywhere: she tottered
in black silk, leaning on
handmaids, on two tortured

fins. At sixty, his sons all
married, grandfather bought her,
Soochow flower song girl.

Every bone in her feet
had been broken, bound tighter
than any neighbour's sweet

daughter's. Ten toes and instep
curled inwards, yellow petals
of chrysanthemum, wrapped

in gold cloth. He bought the young
face, small knobby breasts
he swore he'd not dress in sarong

of maternity. Each night
he held her feet in his palms,
like lotus in the tight

hollows of celestial lakes.
In his calloused flesh, her
weightless soles, cool and slack,

clenched in his stranger's fever.

Shirley Geok-lin Lim

Eunice de Souza

LANDSCAPE

M. assures me she'll be back
to fling my ashes in the local creek
(we're short on sacred rivers here).

The pungent air will suit my soul:
It will find its place among
the plastic carrier bags and rags that float upstream
or is it downstream.
One can never tell.
The sea sends everything reeling back.
The trees go under.

LANDSCAPE II

We push so much under the carpet -
the carpet's now a landscape.
A worm embedded in each tuft
There's a forest moving.

Everybody smiles
and smiles.

Eunice de Souza

Scotsoun

John Greig

We aim to make more available the soun o Scots in literature, music and song on cassette.

This is the statement of intent in the Scotsoun catalogue. At first glance it seems a bit Cecil B. De Mille-ish but when you read through the list of over 85 cassettes, you realise that George Philp and his recording engineer Allan Ramsay have achieved a catalogue of epic proportions.

It all started, so George writes in a recent article, 'Yae forenicht in the simmer dim o' 1973'. He had met Allan in 1970 through the Scottish Language Society and put the idea of the project to him. Their first kistie (cassette) was released on Burns Day 1974 to mark the bi-centenary of Robert Fergusson's death. This was the first tape in the *Makars Series*, covering poets from the fourteenth to the twentieth century. The biggest section in the catalogue with fifteen kisties, this series sets out to draw a thumbnail sketch of the poets' life and achievements, with informed comment on the poems and a selection of the makar's work read by readers "wi a guid Scots tongue in their heid". The series includes Henryson, Dunbar, Barbour, Fergusson, Burns, Ramsay, bringing it up to date with Hugh MacDiarmid and Robert Garioch.

The next largest section is *Other Poets and Poetry Readings*. It concerns itself with more modern poets or with specific dialects, as in *Bennygoak*, poems in a Buchan dialect or *Twa Chiels an a Lass* where Alistair Mackie, William Tait and Ellie McDonald read their own work in Shetland & Scots. There are memorial tributes to Robert Garioch and Sidney Goodsir Smith.

In these series (though I'm sure it applies to all the catalogue), Philp states that "they aimed to help folk appreciate the breadth of Scots literature who, perhaps, have neither the time or the money to study the subject formally". By listening to the kisties they can select the people they might like to read in greater depth and then dig the books out of libraries. George places great emphasis on the 'soun' of the language being at least as important as the content. It's the soun which makes you appreciate the language as much as the written word. The 'voice box' gives the language its distinctive features, and this is one of the main motivations for their work.

The third section, *Music and Song*, is devoted more to soun itself. Philp is proud that they were among the first to record solo piping on kistie and in ten cassettes you can hear the likes of Pipe Major Donald MacLeod MBE, Pipe Major Angus MacDonald, Duncan Johnstone and George Stoddart OBE all giving a selection of airs, Ceol Beag and Piobaireachd. There are recordings of pipe bands like the Dysart & Dundonald Pipe Band and George admits they sell well and help to finance the whole operation.

In the subsection *Songs and Ballads* two of the best kent singers in the Scottish folk revival are represented, Sheila Douglas, with *The Sang in the Bluid* and Andy Hunter with *A Sang's A Sang for aa That*. *Fine Flouers* is a selection of songs from Joan Harkness (successful at the 1979 Traditional

Music & Song Association Kinross Festival) supported by various traditional artists, and there is also *Scottish and Gaelic Songs* by Morag Murray. There is a subsection on choral singing and three kisties of fiddle music from the Kilmarnock and Glasgow Caledonian Reel and Strathspey Societies; also the work of James Scott Skinner presented and played by Hebbie Gray.

The fourth group is *Narratives, Tales, History.* There is a tape of stories from Clydeside & Lanarkshire by Robert McLellan to complement the recent publication (by Canongate) of his stories in book form; there are stories from Fife by Mary Kermack, from the north-east by Gordon K Murray and tenement tales from Springburn by Molly Weir. These kisties are not as successful as Scotsoun would like, but contain some of the best material in the collection. Also in this section comes the story of the Bruce Memorial Window in Dunfermline Abbey, *The Golf Courses at Turnberry*, and *The Roarin Game*, a history of curling in Scotland.

For the Bairns contains eight kisties: recordings from the poems of William Soutar, five tales of the Brothers Grimm (in Scots) and *Wee Willie Winkie*, a collection of Scots songs for children sung by a choir from Hillhead High School. Although not in this section, it is appropriate to mention *Gleg*, a tape for learning Scots or extending your vocabulary. This contains rhymes, riddles, songs and stories with an accompanying book where the stories are printed with a glossary - ideal for children of all ages.

Under *Miscellaneous* are kisties on subjects ranging from *Neeps and Tatties, a monthly guide to growing vegetables,* to The New Testament in **Scots**, passages from the Lorimer translation. One of which was particularly successful, *The Reverend James Currie & Friends* with humorous tales from the Lugton Burns Club Suppers. This is a tape of real 'pawkie' Scots humour, not laughing at the language, as much Scots humour tends to do.

Gaelic is not really the remit of Scotsoun, but they do have a Gaelic tape edited by Derick Thomson containing Gaelic poetry, music and song. The final section, though, is *Scots and Gaelic Combined.* There are songs from both languages by Morag Murray and *Eisd Ceol* - songs in Scots, Irish and Gaelic by Paul McCallum. A tape called *Twa Leids/Da Chanan* was released for the Second International Conference on Languages of Scotland in 1988. Included are poems by Hugh MacDiarmid and Violet Jacob translated into Gaelic by Iain Crichton Smith - the first time these poems had been translated into Gaelic, so the tapes themselves were generating creation. About the same time an article appeared in the *Scots Independent* by Peter Wright, reporting that when William Neill went to a conference in Italy his poems were translated into Italian for the conference. This sparked off an idea for a series of translations of Scots work into other European languages and vice versa. This new venture is to be called the *Euro Makars* series. Glasgow has a large Italian population and the first tape will be in Scots and Italian, including Latin, and features Gavin Douglas's translation of *The Aeneid* into Scots. The tape also includes a poem by Alistair Mackie called 'Don't Cry for Me, Argentina' a description of the Archie Gemmell goal in the 1978 World Cup, translated into Italian in time for the 1990 tournament.

The range of Scotsoun is staggering, while the scale of the operation - two men and a tape recorder - comes under the heading of 'cottage industry'.

industry'. George Philp and Allan Ramsay are two amateurs in the real sense of the word. They do it for the love of it. They have set out to encapsulate the soun o Scots literature, music and song and have achieved a series of 85 tapes, all of which are available. when you listen to the number of 'firsts' George claims, they border on the farcical, but they have achieved them by dedication and because no-one else ploughs this furrow. The BBC have done fine broadcasts in Scots, but the sustained commitment is not there. "Any language into which *The Aeneid* can be translated cannot be dismissed as mere gutter speech or slang", George Philp asserts. Why, then, is it largely ignored in Scotland by the media. Since 1974 Scotsoun have had only two or three interviews on the radio. The Makars series in particular come across as ready-made radio programmes. Seldom is real Scots seen or heard in the media - it's either 'pan loaf' Scots or plain Englis. Contrast this with an interview George did for Radio West Sound (Ayrshire) where they played selections from the Scots Humour tape, during the interview and the rest of the week, creating an unprecedented demand for the tape. Surely this is a case of 'our dog don't eat meat because we don't give it any'? George Philp is sweirt to blame anyone for this state of affairs and feels that a third person to deal with sales might be the answer, but I think it will take more than sales management to influence the media.

Finally I mention two tapes which Scotsoun will bring out shortly. The first was recorded in the School of Scottish Studies at a ceilidh with Belle Stewart, Betsey White, Jimmy Hutchison and Duncan Williamson, a limited edition of 100 costing £5.00. All the monies from this tape go to the School of Scottish Studies Appeal Fund, raising £500. The second is a memorial tape for the late Alexander Scott who did a great deal of work for Scotsoun advising on matters of literature. Clearly, Scotsoun continue to make a substantial contribution to the Scottish literary revival.   John Greig

scotsoun

NEW RELEASES

A Bonnie Fechter - a celebration of the life and work of Alexander Scott (1920 - 1989) with tributes, poems and songs introduced by George Philp

Virgil, Dante, et al - the first in our new *Euro Makars* series, including translations into Scots from Virgil & Dante, as well as translations into Italian of Burns, Garioch and Scott.

Available from Scotsoun, 13 Ashton Road, Glasgow G12 8SP.

James Miller

The Hamecomin

Mary wis comin on for five and she kent a lot. She kent aathin at gied on roond the hoose aa the hours o the day, she kent fit wey her peedie brither wis lookit efter. An she kent fan her faither wis for the sea. For he wid tak doon his muckle leathern boots frae the peg an pit them on ower the thick lang socks at her mither left hingin til warm afore the lowes o the fire.

- It's cauld at the sea.

The boots pit a glamour on Mary. Langer than she wis hersel, she couldna imagine fit it wid be lek til cerry sic clumpan things on your feet. Fan they lay on the grun on their sides, she teeted intil the lang tunnels they made - caves filled aiblins wi gowd.

Bit then, fan her faither cam home, he brocht til her maist byordnar things. A salmon, cauld an siller an smellin o saut watter, wis naethin til fit he brocht times. There wis far mair byordnar things nor a salmon - craiters lek a starnie or a pink ba o spines at he caad a scaddieman's heid.

"I'm awa then. It's a fine calm day."

An he clumped oot o the hoose in his lang heavy boots. Mary watched him frae the winnock for a whilie. Bit fan ye're busy kennin aathing ye canna afford til watch onything lang - an she picked up the ketlin an kittled his wame and garred him purr.

Her mither wis aye workin. In simmer there seemed no end til the work at needit done. Times her faither an mither spoke aboot needin siller. Mary wisna sure aboot siller. She kent it fan she saw it, fan her mither coonted oot pennies and, aince, paper pennies til the grocery van at cam aince a week, or fan a visitor pressed a glitterin sixpence intil her liv an she wis telt til say thank you - bit ayont thae things, siller seemed til hae nae use.

Her mither stopped steerin tatties. "Hamish needs his feed."

Mary had seen Hamish sookan aften eneuch sae she liftit the ketlin again an brocht him oot til the close. Frae there, gin she'd bothered til look, she wid hev seen the sea - calm, sae blue it wis sair on the een, shinin, marked wi glitterin streaks o white lace fan the tide wis runnin. She could hev seen tae the salmon nets set lek arrows alang the shore, an she could hev seen the coble wi her faither an his butties gaein aboot the daily simmer work o gleanin the trapped fish.

Efter a while, her mither cam oot, a pail in her han. "I'm gaein til milk the coo. Ye comin?"

"Dinna want til."

Mary stopped far she wis. Her mither gied intil the byre til get the stoolie for til tak it til the park far the coo wis tethered. This happened every day. Bit fit happened next wis new.

Her mither cam oot frae the byre bit she wisna cerryin the stoolie. Naether hed she the pail. An her face wis set. "I saw your faither. He wis stannin there. He didna speak. He smiled."

Bit Mary kent her faither wis at the sea. She'd seen him gang. He wis aye aff for a whilie. Fit for hed he camen back sae soon?

Her mither didna say anither word bit gied intil the hoose. Mary skippit aff til the byre. Gin he hed camen back she wanted til see fit he'd brocht her. Bit the byre wis empty - teem o aa bit a hen at wis fouterin in the strae. Naethin byordnar - the staas, the hallans, the thekk an its cobwebs high abeen her heid - naethin byordnar.

Her faither an her mither aften said or did things at she couldna understan. This maun be ane o thae things. She gied back til the close and tried til teet in at the winnock. The ketlin pounced on her feet an she skooked doon til grab him an saw some chiel comin. Maggie, the wifie frae the next hoose. Maggie wis auld - Mary heard fowk say this - bit she wis smert on her feet an soon wis stannin richt afore the lassagie.

"Hello, Mary."

"Hello."

Maggie wis gey glum. "Is your mam in?"

"Aye."

Mary gied in efter the auld wifie. Her mither wis sittin at the fire. She lookit up fan she heard feet on the flags.

"Oh Jess, hev ye heard?"

"I ken. I saw him, nae ten meenits syne."

"Oh ma poor lassie!"

Mary saw her mither start til cown, saw tears come tricklin frae the corners o her een. She cried oot, a high gluffed cry. Maggie bent an pit her airms aroond her mither's shoothers.

"It wis a freak wave. They hed nae chance. The sea took them owerboard an filled their boots."

Baith weemin cownin an haudin on til ain anither. Mary didna lek it. She set her teeth intil her lip til stop hersel frae cownin tae bit she didna ken fit else til dae. This wis new - she kent naethin aboot this. She gied oot bit only as far as the door far she could still hear the cownin frae but. Then Maggie cam and bent doon beside her. "Oh ma poor bairn."

The auld wifie stroked her hair an pressed her heid intil her coorse brat. Oot in the park the coo roared. Mary kent fit at wis for.

"Mam's no milkit the coo yet."

Bit Maggie didna seem til listen for she keepit haud o Mary an rocked back an fore.

"Far's dad?"

Maggie took a lang time til answer. "Your dad's gien awa. Your dad's gien awa an he winna be comin back."

The auld wifie strechened.

"Come on." An she smiled, bit Mary could still see the tears on her cheeks. "We'd better milk the coo, eh? Will ye help me? Then we can come back an help your mam?"

Mary wanted til ken far her faither hed gien. He hed been at the sea, he hed been in the byre, and noo he wis gien? Fit way wis he no comin back? In the park she saw at Maggie wisna kent til the coo fa widna stan at first. Mary took aa this in. By this time she sensed at this wis a byordnar day. She kent at things wis never til be the same again. She was learnin fast. James Miller

Naomi Mitchison

TIMOR CONTURBAT ME

Fear like an earwig's nest
Lies between belly and chest
To be soothed by alcohol
Or the historic sense
Of the insiginificance
Of the individual.

Fear like a nest of snakes
Under our breathing shakes,
To be quieted by kissing,
Carefree shopping and spending,
New hat or hair-do lending
Some part of the thing missing.

Fear, the loose spare part
Jolting the tap of the heart,
To be screwed tight by the job
That leaves no time to think
Plough, test-tube, paper and ink -
Keep off, you great slob!

AUSTRALIAN PLACE-NAMES

The meaning of the names is lost
But who, not us, will care?
Those who could tell have slipped away, have crossed
Over the border-line between here and there.
Are these names blessing or perhaps warning?
We do not know.
But would turn it all into polite scorning
Where our amiable suburbs grow.

The great snake tracks have been nicely straightened out.
We need do nothing but brush over the sand.
And we know exactly what it is all about.
Only perhaps up north in Arnhem-Land
Could there be something else? Could our lost names
Assume a meaning that none of us want to hear?
But isn't it best to stop irrational claims?
Or should we listen to something we'd hate to fear?
Is there a secret whisper that blames, that shames?
Ah blank your ears: the meaning might come clear.

REVIEWS

AN UNVANQUISHABLE NUMBER

Radical Renfrew: Poetry from the French Revolution to the First World War, Tom Leonard (Ed), Polygon, 382pp, £25 (£9.95 pbk)

In Tom Leonard Scotland has a rare thing: an honest voice unafraid of the truth and its consequences. This anthology, splendidly prefaced by Leonard's introductory remarks, drives a coach & horses (a Renfrew Ferry?) through the established myth/conception of poetry making, its function and result. What the book claims is that the people of Renfrew, from the French Revolution to the 1914-18 War, have had their experience and what they have had to say about it rubbished from on high by the vested interests of the British State whose aim was/is to keep art in a rarified atmosphere well above the nostrils of the common horde. And up until now the State has been very successful in this. But no more. That period of cultural deceit is coming to a close.

John Robertson, the tragic son of a Paisley grocer - he committed suicide in 1810 - said this about it in his poem 'The Toom Meal Pock':

Tell them ye're wearied o'the chain
   That hauds the state thegither
For Scotland wishes just to tak'
   Gude nicht wi'ane anither.
We canna thole, we canna bide,
   This hard unwieldy yoke,
For wark and want but ill agree,
   Wi'a hinging toom meal pock.
     And sing, Oh waes me!

But somehow thole it they did. It was a tough assignment being working-class, Irish, a woman, in nineteenth century Renfrew. Even for John Robertson, lower-middle-class, things were tight. He ended up joining the Militia in 1803 due to dire poverty. This no doubt contributed greatly to his end. In many ways it runs counter to the spirit of this anthology to pick out any individual voice. It is a *Zeitgeist*. All the 59 named writers and the 9 Anons prove a powerful and eloquent counter to what Leonard cites in his introduction as the jaundiced, yet accepted, view of what poetry is. "The belief is widespread", he writes, "that poetry is not about the expression of opinion, not about politics, not about employment, not about what people actually do with their time between waking up and falling asleep each day; not about what they eat, not about how much food costs. It's not in the voice of ordinary discourse, contains nothing anyone anywhere could find offensive, above all contains nothing that will interfere with the lawful exercise of an English teacher going about his or her duty in the classroom."

That poetry has to be 'taught' Leonard puts forward as being the main root of the problem. The 'problem' being that the poems in Radical Renfrew lay unread, unavailable almost, upon the shelves of the reference section in Paisley Central Library; and Leonard here mentions the conspiratorial nature of releasing un-borrowable books from card indexes. This valuable anthology is just such a release. Here the reader has open access to a suppressed historical experience written in various styles, languages and expressing a wide range of viewpoints. Many of the poems are in Scots and the majority of these in guid Renfrewese. And here the double bind of linguistic snobbery comes into play. It is bad enough from an English educational point of view that the poems are not written in English, but worse that they are written in what, from the establishment point of view, can only be described as uncouth Scots, not 'real' Scots at all. This is also the view of the Scots Language mafia who, too, look down their noses at the West Coast dialect. Therefore the language of the weavers, shoe-makers, navvies, dressmakers, miners etc is held in contempt by those who control and teach poetry, and who construct the cultural value system. It is no wonder that, in the main, working-class Scots are confused about their cultural identity. The further away from 1707 we get the greater this confusion becomes.

The longer the industrial revolution went on the more strident the tone of the writers in Radical Renfrew became, as this short extract from an anonymous dialogue, entitled *Paisley Politics; or Rab and Pate*, makes clear:

O Britain! what accursed scenes
Of feud an' blood thy hist'ry stains!
How many thousands of thy swains
   Have bled and died
To nurse Ambition's dark designs
   An feed her pride!

There follows a long questioning of the value of the Napoleonic Wars to the ordinary folk of Renfrew (and Scotland generally), then a raunchy indictment of the local gentry and clergy. The extract ends:

Ilk virtue frae our lan' hath fled,
Honour is sick, an' Truth is dead,
Justice has broke her sword, the Jade,
   An' burnt her scales,
An' Liberty, like ane afraid,
   Has tane her heels.

So what has become of all this radicalism? Has the spread of education as a right to the mass of the people, as Leonard suggests, "paradoxically led to the deprivation, from them, of much they once held to be valid literature."

Likewise, I would suggest, such a deprivation has gone on in politics. The west coast weavers of the 18th and 19th centuries were in the vanguard of the working-class educational movement and were an extremely well-read and active group. As technology increased and factories proliferated their craft and lives subsequently became dulled and that discoursive tradition sadly lost.

What has not been lost, thanks to Tom Leonard, Renfrew District Libraries and Polygon Publishing, are these vibrant texts. Leonard's work in the poetry of Renfrew, alongside that of William Donaldson in 19th century Scots prose fiction, proves that Scotland's literature is a radically deeper and a more popularly lasting thing than those who rule us would have us believe. This anthology is a shining light from what most of us, up until now, thought was a dark time. These truly are Shelley's "unvanquishable number".

George Gunn

THE STRUGGLE FOR AUTHENTICITY

A Disaffection, James Kelman, £11.95; *Stone Over Water*, Carl MacDougall, £12.95, both Secker & Warburg

Young Mr Doyle the teacher is barely hanging on, and this is a book about it:

He heard them in the staffroom ... they were talking about things that were totally unconnected with anything that could make sense of the world. They were saying things that were just such absolute shite, keech and tollie, such unbelievable rubbish. He had a magazine on his lap, he gripped its pages. He stared at the magazine. It concerned computers. Computers were not sentimental. Aye they were. They were just as sentimental as anything else. It was all a question of hanging on. There were certain concepts. Recursiveness for example. Hang onto that ya fucking idiot.

Introduced in this early passage, sentiment and recursiveness lie at the heart of Kelman's brilliant novel. Patrick Doyle's life - or his ability to make sense of it - is crumbling around him. His point of view, and hence the language of the novel, is suffused with rage and frustration as he struggles to find authenticity and love in himself and the world around him.

Doyle's profession, and his ideals for it, make such disaffection all the more painful, while his education allows Kelman a wider range of inner reference than was possible in *A Chancer*. Doyle is moved by Pythagorean theories of harmony, for example, and the possibility of finding such beauty by 'playing' a couple of conduit pipes that

he has found, like some primal wind instrument. On the other hand, he is haunted by the fate of Holderlin and certain works of Goya, most notably the 'Dog Drowning in Sand', a vision which speaks of his own condition with terrible clarity.

But this is not another *Mr Alfred MA*, although the comparison with Friel's fine novel is a very telling one. There is a sweet decency and a courage in Doyle's struggle, and his heart is not (yet) burnt out. He cares for the children in his classes. He knows love for his brother's family, and engages in a sadly comic affair of longing-at-a-distance with Alison Houston, a married fellow-teacher. As readers we care for Doyle's ineptitude and for his passion, too, and we dread a grim conclusion as the tensions in his inner life become so intolerable that even suicide seems possible. (The novel has a characteristically open ending, all the same, with Doyle running through the wet night, pursued by policemen, thinking 'fuck off' - a kind of dire, dark, ambiguous comedy that Kelman has made his own.)

But this is not simply a book about the psychological strains upon a young teacher, for Doyle's disaffection is a more than personal condition. Part of it is social, for he is caught between his working-class origins and the more middle-class estate of the school staffroom. Doyle's battered car and his ambivalent feelings about it represent his position in this respect, and some of Kelman's best and funniest and most observantly mordant writing goes into the subtle human mislocations which Doyle experiences when he spends an afternoon drinking at his brother's flat with his (unemployed) brother and his pals.

Kelman's achievement as a writer, from the start, has been to master a way of writing about such scenes, *from within*, in a single, undivided language which is capable of both demotic and philosophical force. And the final truth about Doyle is that his disaffection is something like Sartre's nausea. The school-teacher has begun to see through the cultural and social surfaces of his society and his profession, and what he sees has indeed made him sick unto death. Hating the way of the world around him, and simultaneously aware of his own powerlessness, Doyle feels himself to be "caught between the poles" of some terrible magnet. Recursive computer programs loop back on themselves endlessly, and Kelman's prose style uses expletives, obsessive repetitions and unfinished phrases to imitate the loops within his hero's soul. Doyle is decent enough and brave enough to see his plight clearly, but he is not strong enough to overcome it. *A Disaffection* is a finely tragic and darkly comic novel suffused, like Beckett's work, with compassion for the ineffectualness of common pain and, at the same time, filled with a kind of hilarious brave rage.

Carl MacDougall's comedy is a brighter, lighter experience, and although he shares Kelman's concern with the modern state of the Scottish psyche, MacDougall's points of reference are more modishly post-modern, further from Sartre and Beckett, and closer to a point where, say, *Fergus Lamont* meets Ivor Cutler. *Stone Over Water* is an account of lower-middle-class Scottish self-seeking ambition and literary frustration, retold as surreal social satire.

The first clue is the hero's unlikely name - Angus MacPhail - adopted by a bank-manager father with literary ambitions and fated to follow in his footsteps with this book, a combination of private diary and public autobiography whose narrative skips over the years "like a stone over water". MacPhail's adopted family, like his own life and career, is a representative lampoon of his class and times. His stepfather is a disillusioned secret writer, his stepmother eats tranquillisers like Smarties, his sister is a free-loving hippy, and his brother robs banks to promote radical causes.

The fun comes fast and furious with plots within plots and texts within the text, while Angus, now married to frigid Helen, pursues a staggeringly selfish love affair with an impossibly doting younger woman called Miranda. (MacPhail's attitude to women, and the grim way they are treated in general throughout the novel, leaves a sour aftertaste.) The novel's three parts use epigraphs from the Marx Brothers, but the end effect is depressing rather than liberating. *Stone Over Water* is carefully constructed to move us from what seems at first a matter of cheerful 'eccentricity', to a final vision of petty bourgeois dishonesty, spiritual failure and hypocrisy. It works, but finally the reader's sympathies are not so much reversed as lost altogether. For all its surface violence, *A Disaffection* is a deeply compassionate novel; *Stone Over Water*, on the other hand, would seem a cheerful satire (in the spirit of the late Linklater, perhaps) and yet its contemporary gloss is quite deliberately without a heart.

Roderick Watson

GENTLE-MEN OF THE WEST

Walking Wounded, William McIlvanney, Hodder & Stoughton £10.95; *A Very Quiet Street*, Frank Kuppner, Polygon £7.95; *Ridiculous! Absurd! Disgusting!*, Frank Kuppner, Carcanet £6.95

I have noticed an escalating mean and begrudging attitude by fellow Scots towards the writer William McIlvanney, demeaning his carefully constructed novels and political arguments, just on the basis of his deserved commercial success. This was epitomised for me last year when, I

suspect at the behest of his Edinburgh-based publishers Mainstream, he 'came along for the ride' when Kenneth White was being given accolades for, among other things, being 'comparatively unknown'. The stupidity of this contrived situation was compounded when a fellow journalist, full of praise for White (mostly justified), felt obliged to comment that McIlvanney was 'out of place' in the surrounding 'literary' company.

I first read McIlvanney's poetry in the early 70s (*The Longships in the Harbour*). Recently, due to space, I only briefly commented on his collected poems in *In Through the Head* (Mainstream,). May I now categorically praise it, and approach his short-fictions in *Walking Wounded* by reiterating my admiration for this writer's shrewd, sometimes sly way of undermining the cruel and underpinning the compassionate. As he says, "It is of course an operation to unblock the heart but a tricky one, where you have to go in through the head without getting trapped there."

The fictions in his latest book (now in paperback Sceptre £3.99) are not orthodox short stories. They are snapshots and 'home-movies' developed in a private darkroom by a professional cameraman who still manages to sound surprised and delighted at finding familiar faces emerging before him in the daylight. 'I have many images, but they're all populated' McIlvanney said to Trevor Royle before the book appeared in January 1989 (Scotland on Sunday, 1 January 1989). Generous to all men's faults and weaknesses he searches for character rather than depending on the glib stereotypes of caricature.

The pub-bore fighting penury, the dog-besotted weakling. Mike, who knows the "indeterminate sentence" of social insecurity, the hardman "trying to intimidate his grief". He takes the wordsmith's pleasure in using a simple pun to catch the "scribbling rivalry" of children caught in nuptial crossfire. It is his solitary figures that remain even amidst "life dusted rancid" in the fragmentation of such marriages. His own approval of survivors sometimes makes him catch breath before allowing the maimed to be the defeated. This lack of the killer instinct makes some of his female creations one-dimensional and distanced and may be what the usually fair-minded Muriel Grey was talking about when she included him in a sweeping dismissal of 'Glasgow's machos'. For me he is able to enlighten, with an integral gentleness that is often at contrast to his subject matter, "the skulling shapes that feed on mind". *Walking Wounded* is not a series of epitaphs, but a well-crafted sequence of elegies.

Frank Kuppner's *A Very Quiet Street* is subtitled *A Novel, of Sorts.* Allsorts, really. It could be an investigation into the trial of Oscar Slater, a

Jewish immigrant from Germany who was sent down to serve twenty years for the murder of an old lady in 1908. Or of course it could be a tour around the mind of Frank Kuppner who was born at West Princes Street, Glasgow, in 1951, next door to the flat where elderly Edwardian spinster Marion Gilchrist was beaten to death. The book is full of such resonant dilemmas, resonant moments from the author's youth and is, as he himself claims, "resonant topographically" of overlapping moments from half a century earlier. More than once the author wanders off down the wrong track and gets lost. He is very clearly neither giving, nor claiming to give, a last word on the subject. You have to respect a man like that. Certainly it would never occur to anyone to doubt Kuppner's intellectual honesty. Even the mistakes demand that, even when they are not his. Like the author, I found myself turning page after page with tears in my eyes, occasionally moaning with joy, before lapsing into stunned disbelief as "with the" was conjured by publisher Polygon into "wi£1.29" and "these" suspect relatives that populate the pages suddenly become a reasonable "three". All these observations, I note with interest, coincide with the Glasgow Herald review of the book. The reviewer was Frank Kuppner.

Kuppner's second book last year is *Ridiculous! Absurd! Disgusting!*. Divided into three sections it also has an air of self-approval permeating the pages. Erudition and numeracy coexist as the central themes in the opening prose section 'Lost Work'. There are, as the author opines, "dozens of openings for phone calls" provided to the reader; it is densely funny. The second part, 'The Opposite of Dreaming' is in verse. The ubiquitous 'I' tortures out a narrative of sorts in the twenty-four-part movement in four-line stanzas. Only when 'movement' itself wakes the narrator are we allowed to "drift lost among the high numbers". The third part, 'The Autobiography of a Non-existent Person' roams about for 56 pages in a combination of verse and prose. In fact it is a baffling mixture of the blank and the free. As Kuppner says of Lautreamont's writings, it is all 'a rhapsodical prose sequence, and a strange collection of re-worked epigrams'. It is also, as the text admits, a "charming combination of passers-by and absences of passers-by".

I marked the arrival of the author's *A Bad Day for the Sung Dynasty* (1984) as a 'sad day for the word industry': as of now, may I offer an opinion on this latest book. It is disgusting that it is so absurdly ridiculous. Kuppner's books beg for such variations on his themes. He is seamed tight with conundrums and great fun to become ungrammatically involved with . . .

Hayden Murphy

POETRY ROUND-UP

Radio Poems, Robin Bell, Peterloo Poets, £4.50; *The Nor East Neuk*, Sheena Blackhall, Charles Murray Trust, £3.25; *Fite Doo Black Crow*, Sheena Blackhall, Keith Murray Publications, £5.99; *John Donne, You Were Wrong*, Janet Caird, Ramsay Head Press, £4.95; *Against Leviathan*, Norman Kreitman, Aberdeen UP, £2.90.

Two of Robin Bell's three *Radio Poems*, for the speaking voice, have been broadcast by the BBC. The best of them, the most complex and thrilling, has not. 'Chasing the Bear', which the BBC considers "unacceptable for broadcasting", is the dramatic construction of what goes wrong one day in which, as usual, Russian planes, possibly with full war loads, flying surveillance missions across recognisable territory, are being tracked by British and American manned Phantom Jets, again maybe with full war loads. The planes are playing the game, chasing the bear. This, to the poem's characters, the Russian, American and Englishman photographing each other in the air and the Scottish woman officer on the ground in SOC Buchan, is just another ordinary day, and the poem skilfully delineates the perversity of this accepted ordinariness, of being, say, "fifty feet underground" on this "typical March" day. Sets of misunderstandings trigger suspicions on both sides until the luxury of choice is gone; the Russian gunner, or photographer, shows the English and American airmen his mug of soup and marking pens for their cameras, and asks

Do you think we're carrying nuclear weapons?
If we are, do you imagine I'd tell you?
The General Secretary wants to scrap them.
We only have these things because you do.
And you think you have them because of us.

So, subtly, effortlessly, the national meets the personal. The game of chasing becomes a reality in a most convincing way - too like the real thing for the BBC to give it a voice. This is the same foolishness the poem examines. The poem ought to be broadcast.

The other two have successfully met the airwaves. 'Melville Bay', the tale of a Dundee whaling ship trapped in ice in Greenland in the 1830s, told by the young Ship's surgeon, charts a coming together of two people through the rawness of their existence. The burglar voice of 'The Other Thief' makes a personal visit to one particular house, with the listener or reader as his accomplice. 'The Other Thief' is Browningesque in its invitation to uncover the real narrative through the monologue, to show how surfaces deceive, but after the seemingly effortless craft of the other two poems, especially 'Chasing the Bear', in which the tight formality of each section is hardly noticeable in the natural syntax of voice, the reader jibs at some of the rhymes in this piece, though a listener possibly wouldn't.

Norman Kreitman's poetry in his new collection, *Against Leviathan*, throws unforgettable images up, huge imaginative leaps, as here in 'Geology Section, Royal Museum', where he considers the formation of the world's landscapes: "Where the press was most intense the earth sheered/ layered itself into separate histories, then rolled/ and slammed a new horizon against the sky." Such visual strength helps break the distancing that the glazed intellectuality of much of Kreitman's poetry creates. Often his poetry is self-admittedly cold, which makes his love poems all the more outstanding, especially 'Watching as You Go', an enlightening poem. Kreitman's gift lies in his imaginary overviews, the leaps he makes from the abstract to the tangible or vice versa, here in a museum closed for the night: "the ticketed stones/ are left to their space and the vacant air;/ . . .where after dusk a total quiet/ listens to unthinkable time." There is often a sense of Wallace Stevens's modernist tones in his work, of some indefatigable Chinese acceptance.

There is acceptance too in Janet Caird's *John Donne, You Were Wrong*; finality is one main themes and the book resonates with controlled despair, as natural and civilised as the language rhythms she uses. "Out of despair comes a song," she writes. "The roots of making are bitter./ The ploughshare cuts deep, deep." Many poems are concerned with "the clutching claws of time", what she sees as "the seasons' treacheries": "my plant's season of riotous flowering,/ a prodigality of seedlings/ is over." A promising, threatening voyage is a repeated image in these thoughtful and searching poems. Ultimately the argument is between the end of the individual, ("each man is an island", she insists), and the continuation of the natural. "When the skull is an empty shell":

There will be no Schubert.
When the eyes are guttered candles
there will be no Rembrandt . . .
It was not only form and sound
but a beyond that we found
Was it mere trickery, sleight of hand
a mirage to brighten the endless sand?

Is art hopeless, pointless, in the lonely island existence, in the grief of life and its promised end? There are lions and lizards in this collection, a sense of celebration in them like that of Stevie Smith's creature poems. Though the natural is in no way ideal, and roses "re-cycle into humus",

I shall take my digger-trowel and scatter bulbs;
and when time's touch has worn

camber and concrete and the road
is a scar through scrub and ling
down in the valley floor my flowers
will shine each spring.

The individual prevails, in image and voice.

Sheena Blackhall's two recent collections of poetry further demonstrate her prolific talent. *The Nor East Neuk*, with illustrations by the author, begins in a set of "bairn rhymes, breets and bogles"; the voice in her Scots poetry can always be traced back to a form like children's rhyme, with the wit and the element of surprise that's needed as well as the anonymous voice. "The owl's a hoot - his lugs cock oot", she notes, or "the salmon weirs a chyne-mail sark". Her English poetry has this element of surprise in its aptness of metaphor, and often a Plath-like voice in her assembling of metaphors. A bat is a "Lean monk, in perpetual Lent, . ./ A peeling, shriven sprite;/ Or a hurt, gone quiet, healing." 'Seagull', in *Fite Doo, Black Crow*, is another such listing of metaphor into cohesion and revelation. Wit, and passion, and a fine tone of melancholy, pervade both collections. "I delicht in half-licht, in happit, hidden things"; in the same poem she writes, "mair - I like sun, efter rain/ Strikk fire on flinty mica"; the poet of both.

Her Scots poetry has a bite not found so often in her English. Sometimes there is a tendency to approach cliche, descend into whimsy; often she pulls successfully away from it at the last moment, saved by a rawness. "Identity is EYES", she writes. Her poetry repeatedly promises something more than observation: aphorism, meant to be resolution, strikes the reader as refusal to deal with what the images present. Sometimes the poems in *Fite Doo* are hampered by too much punctuation.

The themes of Blackhall's poetry are tough. Birds are as likely to be dead and rotting as alive; seasons are most often wintry. Passion is linked to the earth throughout her work, especially in the compelling poem 'Earth': "Come close, come closer. You must./ My lust is slow, but consuming." In the end mountain and stone are left; men and women as transitory as snow or leaves, the hills, "the altars of renewal". She is at her best in melancholy atmospheric pieces like 'Time Lords', which show the power of nature putting humans in their place; so often her human figures are left between antagonism and belonging. It is telling that the 'Three Arcs of Awareness' set of poems in *The Nor East Neuk* are all awarenesses of darkness. The proliferation of winter images, the melancholy of many poems - again in a likeness to Plath's middle period - give the sense of a soul that longs to escape a seasonal drudgery as well as glories in its dominance, and this culminates in relief at the loss of images of the self, in the fine poem of self reflection 'The Tryst':

Ilk pictur wis masel, a three-in-ain
Triptych o passin time.
The rain began tae dwine,
The pictur slipt frae sicht
An aa wis watter,
Leafiness,
An licht . . .

The anonymous folk-voice in Blackhall's poetry
provides as well as modulates the toughness and
melancholy of her images of living and dying.

Alison Smith

SHORTER FICTION

Into the Ebb - a new collection of East Neuk
Stories, Christopher Rush, AUP, 222pp, £9.50;
Full Score - Short Stories, Fred Urquhart (Ed.
Graeme Roberts), AUP, 198pp, £9.50.

A true poet, Rush sees poetry everywhere,
freeing it both from its more accustomed sources
of sea, sky and earth and from the more mundane
objects that fire his imagination.

All the stories are set around his native East
Neuk of Fife and his habitual focus is the sea. But
within this microcosm teems a diverse parade of
characters and scenes from both history and the
present. And always there is the sea, providing the
constant, ageless canvas on which he paints these
vivid and colourful images so poetically. The old
magic of a place like the East Neuk, where the
stones and waves are witness to a vast movement
of time and people, pervades every line.

Rush looks back at this 'richness' of the past,
almost sighing as he defends the stance of the
poet and dreamer, a stance easier to illuminate
through windows of history and legend. A thread
of sorrow links the stories also, a sense of the loss
of fine old things, of opposition between the
colour of the past and the hollow modernity
which sweeps it away, replacing it with the sterile
and commonplace. In 'Beachcomber' this opposition reaches its most acute expression. The old
beachcomber's repulsive and shallow grandchildren are blind to the Christmas treasure he brings
them from the sea, preferring plastic, mass produced toys to the genuine skull of a whale.

The sea enjoys a sensitive and eloquent spokes-
man as its moods and depths flow through Rush's
pen. His descriptions of the old beachcomber and
his finds reawaken the saltiest memories of
anyone who has enjoyed the pursuit. In this
wonderful story Rush gives reality to the dreams
that rise from the sea. His idea of the sea as a
vast, egoless artist is especially original: "Tireless
old journeyman, the sea tossed a tree from coast
to coast, scrubbing it to a skeleton, and the artist

waves went to work with sculpting fingers that
were free from the egos of self and system. At last
it was washed up on a foreign shore, eloquent of
the sea: a whorled dancer twisted by tides, an
Indian naiad naked as bone, an everlasting moment of pure movement and form."

He can write just as effectively about the
present or, as in 'Tutti Frutti', about the juke box
fifties. Even here though, we see this juxta-
position of past and present in a comparison of
fifties pop love lyrics and some of the finest love
lyrics by Keats and Shakespeare. The adolescent
boy in the story is free to wallow unpretentiously
in the sumptuous lines, even if the lovelorn
teenager is something of a comic figure.

There are times, however, when the beauty
becomes overwhelming. Like a woman in too
many rich jewels, the poetic adornment threatens
to obscure the sensitive skeleton of the structure,
resulting, in places, in a lack of 'story' to uphold
the weight of poetic prose.

Rush's is not an optimistic vision, neither is it
maudlin, but realistic and sorrowful. In *The Saga
of the Green Island*, the slow progression of
history with all its beauty and sorrow is contrast-
ed with the sickness and swiftness of ecological
destruction, of perverted values. Rush makes us
realise the scale of that history, going through
the layers like the rings of a tree. This is an
arresting collection, with some intoxicating passages. It is a pleasure to breathe the salt air that
blows open the pages.

Like Rush, Fred Urquhart has an acute appreciation of things past and passing. Born 1912,
Urquhart's hand arches over colossal changes in
society and he appears to share Rush's view of
their 'benefits'. In many of these fine stories
there is an exquisitely understated sense of sorrow, like a pervasive dusk that serves to highlight
the vivid characters caught up in the change.

In the rural environment, the horse and its
demise as an integral part of farm life becomes a
symbol of that change. In 'Elephants, Bairns and
Old Men', the old man who has farmed with
horses all his life is the victim of brutal insensit-
ivity by his 'mechanised' sons and daughters.
Surrounded, also, by some of the most repellent
and recognisable children to whine their way into
fiction, the old man feels his time is past and he
cannot wait to go. He sits with a dying horse, the
two of them symbolising the same sense of finer,
more colourful, human and poetic things being
superseded needlessly by the brash and insensitive. Pity, which fills the oasis of the stable, is a
difficult emotion for a writer to manipulate
without sentimentality trampling over sensitivity.
But Urquhart, as the best writers do, always knows
the difference and is moving without demanding

superfluous use of the hanky.

Even when his subject is a young, dying, consumptive girl who had been on the verge of marriage, Urquhart never revels in suffering. "At first everybody that I wrote to answered, but pretty soon I didn't get any answers. So I stopped writing and spent all my time knitting." Like Mary in the story, Urquhart is non-judgmental on his characters, he portrays the plethora of human kind without overt criticism: the stories and their characters speak quite clearly for themselves.

Like Lewis Grassic Gibbon, Urquhart breathes the best life into his women characters. Gossips, old maids, grannies and young girls bicker their way, in glorious North East dialect, through the kitchens of the past. Urquhart has a superb command of dialect and presents us with some superbly humorous phrases. These people live and prattle as vividly as Gibbon's did.

In 'The Prisoners', the portrayal of the farmer's wife and her hopes for more sensitivity in her husband should earn Urquhart an honourary 'womanhood'! He understands that self-effacing, objectified love which seems the special preserve of women. He raises what might seem the surrender of the ego or unattractive acquiescence to powerlessness, to nobility, wisdom.

Urquhart moves effortlessly between Scots and English and his cockney is as convincing as his Scots. His talent ranges over comedy, tragedy and ghost stories. At times, the comedy is of the blackest variety, 'Maggie Logie and the National Health', a dark and ticklish example, concerns one Maggie who, determined to get her money's worth from the new National Health Service, does not shrink from a bit of self-mutilation!

Family life with its embarrassment, argument and humour is beautifully observed, reaching peaks of hysterical one-liners. In *Alicky's Watch*, where humour never obscures the sensitive portrayal of the child's world and perspective, two grannies argue over whether the dead daughter should be buried or cremated. Granny Peebles, mother of the deceased, wins the day with the unanswerable argument, "But we have the ground, Sandy. It would be a pity not to use it!"

For me, the rural scenes cling most to the memory with their rich characterisation and dialogue, but the evocation of urban life is equally skilful. The stories portray every kind of excellence as a collection, the spare and delicate treatment of human depression, old age, disillusionment and sorrow, a delight in the farcial, in rich dialect and the slightly wicked. He explores the potential of sitting room, field and factory. Comedy and sorrow are woven together, each highlighting the bright threads of the other.

Gillian Ferguson

THOUGHT IN SCOTLAND

Philosophy and Science in the Scottish Enlightenment, John Donald, £20; *The Science of Man* in the Scottish Enlightenment, EUP, £25; both ed Peter Jones; *Philosophers of the Enlightenment* ed Peter Gilmour, EUP £22; *Enlightenment, Rights and Revolution*, ed Neil MacCormick & Zenon Bankowski, £30; *The Shaping of Scotland*, R J Brien, £7.50, both Aberdeen UP

Conferences produced three of these books, Professor Jones' pair from the 1986 Institute Project Scottish Enlightenment. R J Brien's came of private research, on which he was persuaded to write a book fascinating beyond what its subtitle 'Eighteenth Century Patterns of Land Use and Settlement' implies. Of disciplined mind, he is a lively writer and shows how much there is to see in Scottish landscapes which better use of resources changed radically following 'Enlightenment'.

Peter Gilmour's book, the other not from a conference, has chapters on Leibniz, Boyle & Locke, Berkeley, Hume, Reid, Kant, Adam Smith, Voltaire and Charles Fourier, like encyclopaedia entries collected in handy form, with some flavour of undergraduate-course class-notes worked up. A decent prospect it is, at times, inspired. It matters that starting with an interaction of the humanities with science, the founders of modern thought bore each other's ideas in mind: critically, but not without appreciation. Angus Mackay on how much Reid retained of Hume's ideas is good. There is great literary interest in Prof. Jimack writing on the philosophic basics of Voltaire, and Dr Lloyd-Jones's discussion of Fourier keys into political modernity. Almost all the writers here teach, or recently taught, at Scottish universities.

Christopher Berry's 'Adam Smith: Commerce, Liberty and Modernity', shows Smith seeing human dealings as operations of Nature. Smith as zoologist points as much towards Marx as towards Marketism, society as a Newtonian system of "propensities". Such an approach is at the mercy of bad anthropology, and could foster the hypothetical regime Kemp Smith criticised in his 1919 inaugural lecture, with its outline of more or less the propagandist "Socialist Realism" which Stalin imposed shortly after in place of art.

Tom Crawford on Boswell (*The Science of Man*) rescues Bozzie from false generalisation. If typical of his age, he belonged not only to the 18th century type, but equally to other ages: type gives only vague indications, easily misrepresented: Crawford's literary, personal discussion is better philosophy (love of the wise way of doing things) than (eg) Arthur Donovan's 'Proposal for the Study of Scientific Change' in *Philosophy and Science*, seeking too unitary a picture. Cf

Donald Livingston in *The Science of Man*.

In *Science and Philosophy* C W J Withers writes of agricultural improvement, but the most resonant essay is Paul Wood's story of the struggle for decent science facilities in the University of Aberdeen, today victim of small-mindedness like that of 200 years ago. The book also has decent summaries of key ideas of Tom Markus in architecture and Alexander Broadie on relations between 18th century and medieval Scottish philosophy. Robert Wokler on 'Kames and Monboddo on the Nature of Man' connects with Rudiger Schreyer in *The Science of Man* anent anthropological and linguistic speculation. Andrew Skinner on Sir James Steuart shows how much that great Jacobite economist learned in eastern Europe. Events there now suggest another look at Steuart's rich-country/ poor-country ideas).

The Science of Man amplifies Peter Gilmour's authors on Hume and Reid. It is interesting how inadequate early doctrines of mechanism and the operations of Nature did shed light on how minds work. What Reid maybe got through Hume was that it is not conscious ratiocination or calculation of personal advantage which leads folk, as is the case, to be right about most things. Reid's "Common Sense" is worth study as one account of how minds work when they work right: surely an indispensable precondition of all discussion. His teachings do not aim to vindicate common ignorant presumption. Hume perhaps suffers from having tried at once to correct such presumption and to enable himself to live with its persistence in others: people always get some things wrong.

Beside Prof. Jones on Aesthetics, Passmore (usefully) on 'Enthusiasm', Lehrer and Kuehn on aspects of Reid and Hume, Donald Livingston's 'Hume and the Natural History of Philosophical Consciousness' has wider priority. Livingston spells out "the Humean question (which) must be asked" of "contrary philosophical systems seeking instantiation in the world: liberalism, conservatism, fascism, socialism, Marxism . . . not to mention such forms of cultural criticism such as feminism, deconstructionism, and countless philosophically reflective projects of 'unmasking' and 'consciousness-raising'". Livingston's summary of Hume's analysis of bad ratiocination deserves wide currency. Read it.

That essay is at the centre of human concerns, where Hume's 'success in letters' must be judged. Harvey Chisick's 'David Hume and the Common People' also belongs there, opening up political perspectives. The 'Tory' Hume opposed almsgiving, as what is now called welfarism, because it might delude the recipient as to the reality of the actual human situation. Hume advocated self-sufficiency, but with the stipulation that it must be possible: crucially, startlingly, he insists on no less than "the right to work". Is there enough provision for that in Britain today? Must we always sway madly between welfarism and (for some, i.e. too many) no welfare? Interesting too is Hume's other point, that the argument against popular revolution is the inevitability that it will fail from an incompetence of the "Common People", uneducated and inexperienced, to govern. The real danger (cf. Hume's *History*) is the corrupt noble, petty tyrant, demagogue. As Hume was addressing a comparatively privileged group, he insisted on the viability of some of its preferred pursuits. One might view things differently, but competence against tyrants is essential; as is the attempt of Hume and Adam Smith to comprehend society as the whole of its interactions. What is the alternative to revolution?

See at least *Enlightenment, Rights and Revolution*, papers from a 1989 international conference in Edinburgh. "We hold these things to be self-evident", said the American revolutionaries, having read Francis Hutcheson, properly seen as the father of Scottish philosophy. They also formed universities on a Scottish model which survives better there than here (its breadth boggles pupils from schools in modern Scotland!). The Eighteenth century is sketched in the first section of this book. Other sections deal with 'Theories of Rights', 'Liberty and Equality', 'Equality, Fraternity and the Socialist Revolutions' and 'Analytical Conceptions of Revolution', on the whole heavy going, inevitably. There are references to Africa, to German theory (which like a paper in Spanish surely demanded an English summary!). There is also Virginian Held's 'Feminist Perspective', which concludes with the intriguing observation of how one's attitude to living beings might differ insofar as one could only have fathered them, rather than maybe have given birth to one or more of them after having hosted their early stages in one's belly. A man must see that as a poetic image (though intellectually nothing has primacy over such indispensable thinkings!). It makes an important distinction maybe not borne out by the conduct of some activist women in time of war.

Elsewhere the ills of past welfarism speak out in questioning unweighed claims to rights: the modern individualist's "right to orgasm" may seem a prima facie demand. As good as the rights of the worst-off members of an underclass trapped broke in damp slums unable to have a healthy diet? But Adam Smith's observed phenomenon of sympathy demands observation before there is sympathy: where sense fails to yield reality, thought must cease to yield truth.

Robert Calder

THE APOCALYPTIC MUSICAL RAG-MAN

Ronald Stevenson: A Musical Biography Malcolm Macdonald, Nat. Lib of Scotland, 120pp £8.95

Malcolm MacDonald has always been a champion, a musico-literary 'bonny fechter' who has rescued many a neglected composer. His labour of love has secured recognition for both John Foulds and Havergal Brian. Many living composers have reason to value highly his imaginative sympathy, his individual taste, his encyclopaedic knowledge, and his wide satirical grin, all of which he exercises as editor of *Tempo*, one of the world's leading contemporary-music journals.

In this slender volume on Ronald Stevenson, commissioned and published by the National Library of Scotland to accompany their wide-ranging exhibition of Stevensoniana, one feels these characteristics hard at work. Rarely can the first biographical/critical study of any composer have been so informative, affectionate and funny.

Ronald Stevenson invites such an approach. Of the eleven photo-portraits reproduced, perhaps only the double-portrait of the composer with his wife, Marjorie, fully suggests the warmth, breadth and humour of his personality. Anyone writing on Stevenson takes on a huge task: a great energy, an enthusiast, a composer and transcriber who employs both lyric and the epic modes, an old-fashioned virtuoso pianist who can play on the grandest and most beguilingly intimate levels imaginable, a breezy raconteur, a quirky but sensitive critic and historian, a pugilistic journalist, and a loving family man whose children are themselves artists and craftsmen.

He is writing of one whose life since adolescence has been dedicated to the promotion of the brotherhood of man, and the reactivation of kindly memory in an age of "ever accelerating forgetting" (to use Kundera's phrase), through music, organised sound heard and observed to be the strongest beneficent force in this world. For all of his intellect and torrential eloquence (and this emerges strikingly from MacDonald's text) Stevenson is the opposite of an academic intellectual. Rather he resembles his friend and mentor Hugh MacDiarmid, another great Scottish artist from a working-class background, in possessing the ability to throw together materials taken magpie-fashion from a wide variety of sources, to shape and infuse them with life, and yet to leave a thrilling impression of profusion, chaos almost, provoking the listener to wonder whether the composer is genius or charlatan.

Probably true magicians are both. Stevenson must have laughed at MacDonald's *trouvaille* the term "muchyphony" coined by Soviet composer Miaskovsky for any form of riotous polyphony.

MacDonald captures this element of "joyous stramash", this "strange, merry, friendly Babel of tune, harmony and rhythm" (the terms are Percy Grainger's), this Stevensonian capacity "to pile Pelion upon Ossa and convince his hearers that that is where it belongs". His relation of Stevenson's "avoidance of sonata-form, of musical structures which are rooted in conflict", with his resulting preference for variation-styles, to the composer's pacifism and "global vision", yields some of the best passages in the text.

MacDonald's prologue states that one of Stevenson's primary creative impulses is the "rendering of homage". His own "tenuously chronological" but graphic outline of the Scottish composer's life is just such a rendering. He tells of Stevenson's passion for nature, the Border countryside in which he lives, his childhood wonder at the recorded voices of McCormack, Tauber and Caruso, and his love for their music as sung by his father. He tells of the young man's socialist and pacifist ideals, and his imprisonment in 1948 for conscientious objection to National Service (the composer saw the insides of Preston and Liverpool jails, but also of the dreadful Winston Green and Wormwood Scrubs - he maintained his morale by reading the Bible twice and Schweitzer's *Bach* thrice). MacDonald relates the composer's cherished friendships with Sydney Goodsir Smith, Hugh MacDiarmid, Sorley MacLean, Benjamin Britten, and John Ogdon. He describes Stevenson's creative response to, among others, Busoni, Paderewski, Percy Grainger, F.G. Scott, Edward Gordon Craig, Sorabji, Leopold Godowski, Eugene Ysaye, and James Campbell of Kintail.

The composer will be 62 this year, and his appetite and capacity for work remain vast. MacDonald apologises for obvious omissions: he makes no attempt to describe Stevenson's art as pianist, although he drops hints in his references to the composer's 'Studies in the Art of Belcanto Pianism'. Some who have been lucky enough to hear Stevenson's songs feel they are the best of him: MacDonald doesn't describe them, but concedes tantalisingly "that it might be argued that Stevenson is a very rare case of a miniaturist of genius who completely transcends the limitations that label usually implies."

MacDonald may wish to update this text. But it's hard to imagine that his conclusions will be very different from those presented here. Stevenson, an "apocalyptic ragman" (p85) like his friend MacDiarmid, will surely always be "an idealist with strong roots in reality" (p109). He is a major asset to Scotland and to our straitened age. Anyone who loves Scotland and music should read this book.

Neil Mackay

OSSIAN REVISITED

The Sublime Savage: A study of James Mac-Pherson and The Poems of Ossian, Fiona J Stafford, EUP, 208pp, £22.50

Fiona Stafford's study of MacPherson is radically informative. While I remain more sceptical than she about the Ossian phenomenon, I applaud the intelligent industry with which she has set the man and 'his' poetry in the context of its time. The first half of the book concerns MacPherson's psychological evolution and his stylistic development. His childhood experience of post-Culloden genocide ("An army of fiends let loose from Hell, with Lucifer at their head") has obvious relevance to his subsequent mythical, morbid treatment of tribal dissolution. Even more revealing is her examination of the influence on MacPherson of his period as an Aberdeen undergraduate. Given to pursuing a pragmatic, innovative educational policy, Aberdeen was, ironically, a fraught centre of the 18th century's contradictory impulses regarding the primitive and the progressive. Professor Blackwell's *Enquiry into the Life and Writings of Homer* was surely a key text in providing MacPherson with a model of the communal virtue and epic form which he later alleged belonged to primordial Gaeldom. Indeed, he developed a dangerously facile sense of Hellenic and Hebraic analogies for his Highland paradise lost.

Stafford believes that it is precisely such false analogies which lie behind not only the doubtful virtues of MacPherson's late style but the obsessive problem of the authenticity of his sources. The content of MacPherson's poetry remained remarkably constant in its hot-house melancholia, its personal and national compensatory fantasies and its vision of primeval Highland life designed for a cosmopolitan market. Stafford traces its formal evolution through the maladjustments of conventional 18th century poetics to the discovery of the free-flowing rhetoric and form of the Ossianic 'epic'. "By dismissing his principal sources as corrupt, MacPherson felt free to 'restore' the Gaelic poems to what he thought they ought to have been." Inevitably what they ought to have been was remarkably like the rhythm and language of the King James Bible.

Equally, Stafford points out that there is nothing of genuine epic form in the Ossianic fragments. In both tone and form it is a definably eighteenth century text. "Despite its epic pretension, *Fingal* is a sprawling work, held together not by unified action or theme but by the presence of the narrator. As in Sterne's contemporary novel, *Tristram Shandy*, a baffling series of recollections is made coherent only through the

development of the narrator as the focal point." She clearly shows that MacPherson is no window to the past but a mirror in which we can see the 18th century peering anxiously but narcissistically at itself. In an 18th century Scottish context it could be argued that the problem of the authenticity of MacPherson's authorship stems not from his alleged sources. Rather, because of his responsiveness to earlier Scottish achievements and contemporary desires, these texts could be defined as a collaborative venture by the Anglicised genteel literati. Thus MacPherson builds on a highly marketable Highland primitivism derived from Mallet and Thomson's reworking of Martin Martin's Hebridean travel writings. Equally, Hugh Blair's rhetorical theories underpin Ossian. In reality such a sensibility was as dismissive of genuine Celtic poetry as it was of the vernacular language of Lowland Scotland.

For the rational eighteenth century the Highlands proved an irresistible playground for repressed fantasies. The past was another and far more indulgent country: "She came, in all her tears, she came, and drew it from his breast. He pierced he white side with steel; and spread her fair locks on the ground. Her bursting blood sounds from her side: and her white arm is stained with red. Rolling in death she lay and Tura's cave answered her sighs."

What a peculiar yet predictable national epic it is. Unlike Arthur there is no promise that Ossian will come again. This is the whole point: Scotland is irreversibly severed from its past. In no small part this contributes to Tom Nairn's paradox in *The Break Up of Britain* regarding the non-emergence of nationalism in Scotland during the European romantic revolution. It also contributes to MacPherson's antipathy to the American Revolution. In the dire melodramas of MacPherson's early poetry there appears the figure of the Highland ingenue who destroys himself through vile ambition. MacPherson's life, if not his art, is a mature study of this theme.

Andrew Noble

THEATRE ROUND-UP

I have always thought that the picturesque charm of South Queensferry has been rather spoiled by the two obtrusively large bridges; and one wonders what Jonathan Oldbuck or David Balfour would have made of the "designer burgers" on offer at the Hawes Inn these days. Earlier this summer, I was making my way to the said Inn along with a few other people and a bagpiper, when our progress was interrupted by raucous cries and a descent of kilted roisterers from the hillside. As we move insensibly but steadily towards a Theme Park Britain, such happenings will doubtless become more commonplace; but in this case the episode was part of a large dramatic entertainment provided by the catchily-named Forth Rail Bridge Centenary Theatre.

It has to be said that the three-and-a-half hours of *The Ferry Play* were not uniformly enthralling, and the fellow who was afterwards heard to remark, "I thought it was the *Tay* Bridge that had the disaster" did have a certain point. Nevertheless, this doleful extravaganza makes a good starting place for a consideration of two related and increasingly topical questions, of which the first concerns "community theatre".

There has recently been an upsurge in community theatre, in places as disparate as Dundee and the Borders. For many reasons this is of course to be welcomed; but I think we could profitably give some thought to exactly what kind of community theatre we should best encourage.

Part I of *The Ferry Play* makes a good example of large-scale community theatre, reasonably well-funded and with the benefit of a professional input. It took the form of a stroll along the South Queensferry waterfront, punctuated with stops for short playlets (provided by various local writers) treating with bits and pieces of local history, and intended as a popular commemoration of the borough and its people.

All well meant, but alas largely inaudible, and the visible acting inevitably at a level between a school play and an amateur drama festival. It is no belittlement of the efforts of the massed children and others involved to say that such projects are really only of interest the immediate community, able to note wee Johnny there in the second row, or Jeannie at the back in her braw dress. Others are liable to be left unriveted.

This drawback was even more prominent in another cast-of-thousands production, Theatre Workshop's *The Lightning Plebiscite*, about old Leith and its forced merger with Edinburgh. It was again a worthy undertaking to which immense labour had been devoted, and again fairly dismal as regards overall quality. The Workshop's director, Adrian Harris, has a commendable policy of combining performers from all sections of society, including the elderly, ethnic minorities, and the mentally handicapped. This has great social value, but makes it unlikely that the result will be of much interest to someone merely looking for a good evening's theatre.

By contrast, I well remember how under a previous regime the Workshop did regularly put on excellent (and widely popular) community productions, but this was achieved only by taking a fairly elitist approach. At the core of these productions, playing the main parts, were half-a-

dozen professional actors, and although plenty of locals were brought in, they were used according to ability. The results were invariably lively and well-acted, but a lot of the participants were deployed only, for example, in crowd scenes.

Was this a better way to do things? I don't think there can be any hard-and-fast answer. But at the same time, theatre surely isn't much without an audience, preferably an audience enjoying themselves and really getting something out of the play; and in that respect at least, the 'elitist approach' certainly has powerful advantages.

Part two of *The Ferry Play* exemplified a genre that might be called "professional community theatre". *Bridging the Gap* was a fully professional piece commissioned from Hector Mac-Millan, and one must say at the outset that writing a play to commemorate the centenary of the Forth Bridge is a daunting remit. (Though not unprecedented; I recollect being told by the late Cedric Thorpe Davie how he was commissioned to write a piece of music to celebrate the opening of the Forth Road Bridge "to be played at an official ceremony in the Cameo Cinema, Toll-cross"; even after many years, that last bit seemed to rankle.)

Bridging the Gap was a Chinese doll affair, in which the actors play a group of amateur actors putting on a play about the bridge's opening. It was fun as far as it went, which was not, however, very far; and MacMillan seemed unable to decide whether the bridge was a symbol of capitalist exploitation, a triumph of Scottish engineering, or of the labour and blood of workers. He made a few daringly smashing blows at Victorian figures like as the Prince of Wales; amazingly, such violently contentious sentiments appear to have gone unnoticed by the Establishment at large, not even eliciting a protest from Mary Whitehouse.

"Professional" community theatre - professionally-written and performed works usually put on in the community which is their subject - has become increasingly common of late. The most conspicuous example is Tony Roper's perfectly awful *Steamies* about old Glasgow wash-houses, immensely popular on account of its cloying sentimentality, variety-show format, and its refusal to make even the most minimal intellectual demand on the audience. (Donald Campbell's plodding *Musselburgh Reel* was at least sufficiently convoluted of plot to force *some* effort of thought upon the audience.) But what I find actively distasteful in something like *The Steamie* is its wholesale discounting of the grim, drab, unremittingly harsh conditions under which past generations, and particularly the women, had to exist; there was undoubtedly a triumph of the spirit, but let us have no illusions that we should be glad that age is behind us. One wonders whether future kailyarders will reminisce in similarly loving vein about the violence, drug addiction, Aids and poverty which nowadays characterise the housing estates of Edinburgh and Glasgow.

This leads on to a good attempt at a modern community play, which did not flinch from the problems and was, though professional, done with considerable local input. A few years ago, some enterprising people offered tours of Edinburgh which, eschewing the more popular sights, concentrated instead on the city's generous endowment of slums, squalor, decay and dereliction. *Trade*, put on by the ever-enterprising Oxygen House Company, was driven by a similar desire to deliver a not-so-gentle reminder of what daily existence actually entails for significant numbers of our fellow-citizens; and in paricular, those whose sole cashable asset is their bodies.

It was a dramatic collage, a series of snapshots of life at the tattered and desperate fringes of society. Prostitution was the unifying theme, but by delving a little into the backgrounds of the 'street workers' (and their clients), much else was brought briefly but sharply into focus: including (inevitably) Aids, massage parlours, homelessness, rent boys, abortion, place-of-safety orders, drugs, rape, battery and (offstage) murder.

This intimidating range of topics was approached with a marvellous blend of objectivity and passion. No preaching, no moralising here, no heavy-handed political gesturing; merely a plain, unvarnished representation of people's lives - skilfully worked up into dramatic vignettes of strong realism and power. I still can't get quite used to their ridiculous name, but if the future of Scottish theatre lay with Oxygen House alone, one could be confident it was in good hands.

Finally, one production that ought not to pass unmentioned. Chris Hannan's *Elizabeth Gordon Quin*, set during the 1916 Glasgow rent strike is really more a play *per se* than a piece of community drama, but is an outstanding example of how to bring a community to life on stage. This summer the play was taken on tour by Winged Horse. Hamish Glen's production is, i think, even better than the original one, losing nothing of the play's strength whilst making the humour seem brighter and fresher. The brilliant cast was led by Ralph Riach as the affable Mr Quin, trembling exquisitely between comedy and pathos, and by Eileen Nicholas as the eponymous heroine. The latter is invariably so ridiculously good that it is difficult to say much about her, except to express the wish that she won't be tempted to stand for Parliament; for apart from the loss to theatre, it would be a shame to upstage Glenda Jackson.

Alasdair Simpson

PAMPHLETEER

Amphibious Landings by Robert Roberts (National Poetry Foundation, 27 Mill Road, Fareham, Hants PO16 0TH, £3.90) is a collection of highly-crafted, sculptured poems which use of traditional rhyme and rhyme patterns. Many of them deal with everyday domestic subjects and situations, evoking a lost pre-war world of childhood. Roberts is concerned with the 'Background Music' of his life - the poem this title belongs to reveals how, unconsciously, seemingly trivial happenings and experiences penetrate our lives, subtly shaping character and personality. The poems uncover Roberts' own personal influences - classical myth, painting, Romantic and Georgian poets; implicit in them all is the paradox which memory, and the past, invariably brings, in 'Magnificent Men': "the paradox/ That, being human, they must be/ Strapped in - in order to float free". These poems are rich in visual description, and at the same time reach deep inside the mind.

The picturesque is to be found again in *Ten Letters to John Muir* by Terry Gifford (Burbage Books, 56 Conduit Road, Sheffield S10 1EW, £2.50). John Muir, a Scot, was the founder of the Yosemite National Park in 1890. Recently, in Scotland, the John Muir Trust has been set up to protect the Highlands, and it is to this Trust that all proceeds from the book will go. The poems themselves are written as letters from a modern visitor to the Park with the purpose of updating John Muir on its state. They evoke with clarity and beauty the splendour of the landscape, with memorable imagery:

There came this aura
Over the dome top
In which there danced
The insects of the air
shining on silver wings
True angels of light

The poet juxtaposes the untouched land of John Muir with the busy tourism of the present day. He feels disgust at the half-tame monkeys begging for food, because something has changed, the spirit of the place has altered. These poems have moments of remarkable insight "Back in town/ I buy an Indian pot washed with the colours/ Of a sky where the sun set long ago" - which are tinged with regret, for the loss of something which cannot be defined, a loss, perhaps, of newness. These poems are accomplished and interesting; the cause they support is a bonus.

More accomplished poems come from Ida Matthews in *A Night Atween Weathers* (The Pentland Press ltd, Kippielaw, by Haddington, East Lothian, £5.00). The introduction to this collection has been written by George Mackay Brown, who says of the poet that "She knew that, in addition to the urgings of the spirit, poetry was an affair of workmanship and craft". The poems are marked by their precision of structure; they are short poems which capture a moment, a thought or an emotion. Many of them are concerned with old age, and the sadness of not being able to do all that you were once capable of. It is a state of no return: "I have been young and now am old." The imagery of the poems is at once concise and infinitely expressive - to the elderly, days are/ jewels strung on a fragile thread/ to be handled tenderly one by one." Religion is important to the poet - faith inspires both her work and her life and is expressed in several poems. One poem, 'Crisis', is alarmingly topical in subject, being concerned with man's inevitable destruction of his planet. These poems are controlled and perceptive - beautiful yet poignant explorations into the sadness and joy of life.

Mark Gallacher's *More than a Dedication* (Envoi Poets, Pen Fford, Newport, Dyfed, Wales, £1.80) is a deeply personal collection of poems to and about the poet's father. His father, Gallacher discovers, influenced him more through what he didn't do than through anything he did. They are sad poems about loss and exile, through which the poet begins to come to terms with his difficult relationship with his father. He writes: "Opening up sometimes leaves you hurt". In these poems he opens up and exposes his deepest, most painful emotions. The theme is handled with sensitivity, and sentiment never becomes overpowering. This collection is profoundly moving.

London Toes by Brian Whittingham (Crazy Day Press, 5 Earn Avenue, Renfrew, £1.20) is a collection of highly contemporary poems. Many of their ideas are interesting and the language is often experimental, but any good points are spoiled by the proliferation of spelling errors throughout the text: mistakes such as "potatoe", "pigions", "arguement" and "pyscopath" are avoidable and extremely irritating. The poems, on the whole, dispense with any kind of punctuation, which makes many of them seem formless and drifting. The visual layout seems arbitrary and without any relation to what the poem is actually about. In many cases, the experiment simply does not work.

The Bolo Boys by Mac McIntosh (Victoria Press, 50 Buckland Road, Maidstone, Kent ME16 0SH, £4.50) is quite different. McIntosh fought in the Scots Guards in the Second World War and was a prisoner of war in Germany. These poems are not beautiful. They are factual and stark, and their bleakness effectively conveys the atmosphere they seek to describe. They show little emotion; instead the poet relates the horror of war, and leaves the reader to find his own reaction. Not poems to be enjoyed, they are nevertheless worth reading. Throughout there is a pervasive sense of the sheer waste and futility of war. In the tradition of war poetry in English, McIntosh has more in common with Sassoon than with Owen, but without the former's grim humour. These are harrowing poems, awful in their realism, but with a message for everyone. They are a little rough in technique, but so much war poetry is unpolished, and benefits from it. McIntosh seems to care more about the subject than the form of his poetry, a tendency which is understandable in such a context.

Four pamphlets from Satis are mixed in subject and method. My main objection to Matthew Mead's *A Roman in Cologne* (Satis, 14 Greenhill Place, Edinburgh) is that the print is difficult to read. The poems are spare and unadorned, with some interesting ideas, such as the startling conclusion to *Confrontation*: "God hates the human race." But the structure of many poems is loose, and lines tail off uncertainly. The poems with end-punctuation cohere better, and communicate ideas more effectively. I found a similar problem in *The Tightrope Walker* by Christa Reinig (Satis) where again the structure seems undefined. These poems are translations from the German - descriptive, often factual, and concerned with a sense of division and danger and the disparity between fiction and reality.

Songs from the Old Folk's Home by Christian Geissler is also a translation from German. These poems are untitled, and the divisions between them often obscure, so that the poems run into each other, an appropriate device for poems about the confusion and monotony of old age. The sterility and emptiness of the Home is emphasised. These are sad poems about lonely people, trapped and waiting for death. The final pamphlet from Satis, *If a Glance Could Be Enough* by Gael Turnbull, is more hopeful in tone. These are carefully-crafted poems of place and tradition, which look back to the past. Experience is related in a way which is instantly identified with. The poems are rich in colour and image, conveyed with quiet control.

Three collections from Writers' Groups show immense variety in subject and style. The first, *Pencil Points*, from Gorebridge Women's Writing Group, contains short stories, 'diary pieces' and poetry. Though entertaining, the pieces often seem short on originality. The best by far is the amusing story in Scots, *The Accident* by G W Nichol, with its lively dialogue. Overall, this is an uneven mixture - some mediocre pieces, interesting ones, and some which are quite accomplished. The best pieces, on the whole, are placed towards the end of the book, which seems a pity.

Revolving Showcase, by Falkirk Writers' Group, is more substantial. Much of the poetry follows a very conventional rhyming pattern, which becomes tedious at times. Again the quality is inconsistent, but there are some very good pieces, particularly about old age, which articulate genuine experiences and emotions. There is more variety of genre here than in the Gorebridge book - the list includes prose articles, science fiction, children's stories and personal essays. The tone is generally light-hearted which makes this an enjoyable read. *Shouts and Whispers No 2* from Barrhead Writers' Group is also entertaining. The supernatural is a favourite topic, and again the variety is immense. The poetry is rather trite, but the short stories are more impressive. Emotion is handled well by many of the writers, and two stories by Margaret Bruce deal skilfully with childhood experience. There is a lot of humour, particularly in 'H P - A Broch of a Boy', a very funny look at history with some truly cringeworthy puns. The striking feature of this collection is its variety of style and content - it is amusing and sometimes thought-provoking.

Finally, *The Crack and the Cant* by Michael Gregson with Kay Deas (Gadgie Publications, 18 Alder Place, Culloden, Inverness IV1 2LG, £3.50) is a 'dictionary' of contemporary Highland speech. It doesn't claim to be comprehensive or objective, and it is deliberately political. Cant is language used by gypsies, much of it of Romany origins, and this is the most interesting part of the book. For example, 'naiskill' means 'father', 'pannie' is 'water' and 'peeve' is a drink (usually whisky). Elsewhere are intriguing if not wholly serious items, like 'crisp packet - unorthodox condom', and 'Cromarty Firth - oil rig reserve'. Occasionally the definitions become fascetious and irritating, such as "Kinloss - air force base near Forres responsible for sending out large numbers of very-low-flying fighter-bombers to deafen or alarm us or waste our taxes, in perpetuating the myth that the Russians are about to invade us." Then it seems as if Gregson is sacrificing linguistic aims for cheap political digs, but otherwise this is a fascinating and valuable book.

Angela Finlayson

CATALOGUE

Pride of place goes to an edition of 'Rauf Coilyear', *The Tale of Ralph the Collier* edited by Elizabeth Walsh (Peter Lang, Jupiterstrasse 15, CH-3000, Bern, Switzerland, DM 64.50). This alliterative romance, from the late fifteenth century, comes with full scholarly apparatus, introduction, commentary, extensive notes with due reference to other texts, literary history, context, folklore connections, exotic references such as to "tiger", glossary. Dr Walsh is good at imparting background information and analysis in accessible terms. If she can sound a shade ingenuous, that is mere lack of affectation. A rare virtue. The verse of *Rauf* is an instrument worth emulation for its sweep like a long prose sentence, but nonetheless lilt or lift. Less than masterpiece, such poems still give sustenance.

The Comic Poems of William Tennant, ed. Maurice Lindsay and the late Alexander Scott (Scottish Academic Press, £15) includes of course 'Anster Fair' (1812), Tennant's most famous work, in full, with its anticipations of Byron. Rather piled-up as his verse can be, the also lengthy 'Papistry Stormed' makes a modest virtue of this; with bursts of very effective strong Scots, at times shooting over the top into broad burlesque. Hardly an outstanding poet Tennant still ought to be available. Not as model for the coamick, but trying Scots resources useful for many purposes. *Literature and Literati, the Literary Correspondence and Notebooks of Henry Mackenzie, vol 1 Letters 1766-1827*, ed. Horst W, Drescher, comes from Peter Lang (DM 75). Mackenzie lived from 1745-1831. This book is a mine of Scottish cultural references.

Bruce Griffiths' *Saunders Lewis* has been reissued (University of Wales Press, £4.95). Beside the great *Presenting Saunders Lewis* from the same publisher, it gives a more than adequate account of one of the major writers of this island this century. Though he wrote in Welsh Lewis is now accessible, worth setting against his admiring near contemporary MacDiarmid. A major playwright (now extensively available in English translation from Christopher Davies of Swansea), a great, sparingly productive poet, agitator for Welsh and European culture as mutually revelatory, nationalist who knew better than any the evils of nationalism - no political cause is any good that does not serve human freedom - his resolve was rooted in a deep sense of the tragic and not in any hollow emotionalism. He was a very great man. "Language or dialect we have none, we recognise no insult,/ And the masterpiece we gave to history is our country's MPs."

William Gerhardie (1895-1977) was something of a victim of the literary scene, and as failed genius a potentially good topic for the biographer. He powered his considerable gifts with something on the edge of wilfulness and not quite grown-up. Dido Davies' *William Gerhardie* (OUP, £25) is the sort of efficient biography which does him justice, neither academically nor in popular terms self-indulgent. The not quite English altogether eccentric is one of the more endearing literary sub-species. Some think Gerhardie by no means a failed genius, certainly in such prodigious novels as *Resurrection* and *Of Mortal Love*.

Fitzroy Maclean might feel slighted that his illustrator, John Springs, gets star billing here. The former's *West Highland Tales* (Canongate, £7.95) is a fairly straightforward retelling of some favourite tales: which can be done only so well, and is here done most respectably, perhaps to the good of the insufficiently attended repertoire. But the wit and allusion in the line-drawings are astonishing. This column as *addenda* can plead weariness of, nay scunneredness with pastiche period prose. Charles Palliser's ambitious *Quincunx* (Canongate, £14.95) alas landed with a near 800-page thud on a catalogue-artiste allergic to such performances. A lighter thud and novel is Robert Nye's *The Memoirs of Lord Byron* (Hamish Hamilton, £11.95), no less pastiche in prose, far less substantial than *Quincunx*, which can at least be seen as a serious attempt at (among other things) historical fiction. Todd McEwan's *McX* (Secker & Warburg, £12.95) goes in the other direction. As an attempt to be too clever by haufs and hauf-pints it has succeeded. Parody of parody, knowingly quirky prose-poetry, quasi-satiric, the doubtful point of this "romance of the door" is likely not worth getting. McPint and his pals remain up in the (very foggy) air.

Richard McKane's *Anna Akhmatova - Selected Poems* (Bloodaxe, £7.95) isn't clever enough. Instead of "No, this isn't me, it's somebody else who's suffering" ('Requiem' II) there is "No, this is not me, someone else suffers." Vitiated now and then by pedantic inadequacy of that sort, failure to honour English idiom, repeating instead Russian idiom, this book is still not all that bad. The clumsinesses can be ignored, they're not ubiquitous, there's no cheap seeking of effects absent from the original. Worth a look too is *Woman between Mirrors* by Helena Parente Cunha, a Brazilian writer (b.1929) who uses novelistic methods and interior dialogue to question general statements about "Woman", referring them to the case of one woman in her native place, at her time of life, etc. specifically. The translation is splendid, and like most interesting books supposedly in an "experimental tradition" (sic! - the blurb's phrase) it works at the same fundamental level as the simplest lyric poem. No pretence.

Ruth Brandon's *The New Women and the Old Men*, 'Love, Sex and the Woman Question' (Secker, £16.95), may in unfair comparison seem inferior to Parente Cunha's book. It combines biography, social history and feminist analysis, according to the accurate blurb: there are comparisons between the lives of Eleanor Marx, Beatrice Webb, Rebecca West, &c., and H.G. Wells,

Havelock Ellis, among other men. It seems too much a writing-up of case-studies, not dogmatic generalisation, but also not doing enough justice to specific situations. Perhaps nobody should take seriously F. Gonzalez-Crussi's *On the Nature of Things Erotic* (Picador £4.99). Will that over-lyrical hispanic essayist be convulsed with rage to hear his disquisitions on androgyny, the Marquis de Sade, an ancient Chinese text &c. deemed a jolly sport? He takes *something* seriously, but what? The Divine Marquis at an orgy, Old Nick presiding, versus Hugh Hefner on a bed with an engine in it and a Penthouse pet on it; and a colourfully-named author aghast at the banality. The ceremony of guilt has withered in the light.

Memories and Portraits, and *St Ives* (both £4.99) mark an interest in Stevenson from Richard Drew Publishing, who have also published a paperback of Jenni Calder's *R.L.S. A Life Study* (£6.99). Ms Calder has also essayed a new ending to *St. Ives*, which was left unfinished, and which presumably will be used soon in the 'major television series' of which the blurb speaks. In an essay on dreams Stevenson did a good pastiche of William Dean Howells, whose New York novel *A Hazard of New Fortunes* (1890) is an O.U.P. World's Classic at £5.95. Same series but twice the size, the simultaneously republished *Nicholas Nickleby* is the same price as Howells' book: sales economics. Perhaps such standbys as Fenimore Cooper (*Last of the Mohicans*, £3.95) and Maupassant (*A day in the Country and Other Stories*, same price) fund the less famous items: Wilkie Collins' 1862 shocker *Basil* (£4.95), the now-touted Trollope's colossal *Ralph the Heir* (£5.95), the profound melancholy stylishly written *The Good Soldier* of Ford Madox Ford (£3.95). Ford tutored Conrad in English prose, the medium he composed in with a musical, rhythmic-expressive sense which brings to mind the tread of Rauf Coilyear. Ford might have admired the prose of F.G. Wood, precise and cultured in startling contrast to the dire jacket, blurb and title of *Kidnap in Rio* (£6.95, Merlin Books, 40 East St, Braunton, Devon EX33 2EA). Supposedly playing Watson to a Holmesian Colonel, the narrator of this report-like novel is a more interesting character study himself. Perhaps he represents the octogenarian author.

Moving Worlds, ed Edensor and Kelly (Polygon, £7.95) is oral history, twenty Edinburgh residents from different lands and times: Lithuanian Jew born in 1897, latterday Ukrainian, Allende period Chilean exile, Iraqi Kurd, others. Sikh and Lithuanian Jewish Edinburgh Scots are lively dialects. The bases of such collections can be dodgy, but editorial control is acute, the book is to the point, the contributions of great interest.

NOTES ON CONTRIBUTORS

Fleur Adcock: New Zealand feminist poet.
John Agard: Actor and writer born Guyana 1949; came to Britain in 1977. Describes himself as 'poetsonian'. Writes for children and adults.
Marsha Prescod: Prominent young Black writer from Caribbean background in London.
Ama Ata Aidoo: Former Education Minister in her native Ghana, now in Zimbabwe. Playwright, author and poet.
Rafiq Azad: Bengali poet.
Mohammed Bashir: Native of Pakistan living in Glasgow since 1960. Head, Strathclyde Regional Council Interpreting Service.
Azouz Begag: Algerian novelist, born 1957 at Villeurbanne, Dr Economics. Winner of le prix Sorcieres in 1987 for Le Gone du Chaaba.
James Berry: b. Jamaica, 1924, came to Britain shortly after WWII and now the doyen of Black writers in Britain; prominently involved with the Arts Council and has published several books of poetry.
Angus Calder: Tutor in English at the Open University. Poet and critic.
Patrick Clark: Retired schoolteacher. Winner, Scottish Poetry Competition run by Spectator/-Johnny Walker in 1984.
Nuala ni Dhomnhaill: Born Lancashire 1952, raised in Dingle Gaeltacht in Kerry, now lives in Dublin, published 2 books of poetry.
Saqi Farooqi: Bengali poet.
Richard Fletcher: Lives Glasgow, writes fiction and poetry. Takes Writers' Workshops at Glasgow U. where he works, writing educational software.
Sam Gilliland: Writer, broadcaster born Ayrshire 1939, organiser Scottish Open Poetry Competition. Published UK, India, Spain & USA.
John Greig: Folk singer and producer of tape magazine, Songs from Under the Bed.
Kaiser Haq: Volunteer in Bangladesh Army during war of independence; teaches English at Dhaka. Published 2 books of poetry and translated Shamshur Rahman; editing anthology, Contemporary Indian Poetry for Ohio State UP
Michael Henry - English poet, Cheltenham.
William Hershaw: Fife poet & English teacher born 1957. Published books of poetry include High Valleyfield, Glencraig, May Day in Fife.
Miroslav Holub: b.1923, a distinguished immunologist as well as one of Czecholsovakia's great writers, despite official disfavour. Vanishing Lung Syndrome to be published shortly by Faber.
Jackie Kay: Grew up in Glasgow, attended Stirling University. Now establishing reputation in Scotland as exciting young Black writer.
Lotte Kramer: Born Germany, came to England as child refugee 1939; four books of verse, latest The Shoemaker's Wife (Hippopotamus Press).
Mike Jenkins: Poet, editor Poetry Wales.
Marianne Larsen: Danish writer and poet.
Shirley Geok-lin Lim: Malay Chinese, teaches at California Santa Barbera. Commonwealth Poetry Prize for Crossing The Penninsula in 1980.
Taban Lo Liyong: b.1938 Sudan. First African to win Master of Fine Arts from Writers' Workshop at the University of Iowa, published books of stories, poetry, essays and folklore.
Liz Lochhead: Glasgow born poet & playwright.
John Lyons: Short story writer and illustrator. Lives in Manchester.
James E McCormack: b. Blantyre 1934 of Irish parents, teaches in Glasgow Secondary School. Published Scotland, Ireland, Canada, England.
aonghas macneacail: Born Uig, Skye, prominent Gaelic poet, writer and broadcaster.
Martin Marroni: Scottish writer and poet.
James Miller: Native of Caithness, lives near Inverness. Published fiction, travel-writing, history. Has written professionally for the theatre.
Naomi Mitchison: Author of over 70 books. Tribal mother to Bakgatla tribe, Botswana.
Dea Trier Morch: Danish novelist and travel writer, artist and head of Danish Writers' Union.
Hayden Murphy: Poet, editor of Broadsheet, freelance writer & reviewer.
William Neill: Prominent Scottish poet, writes in English, Scots and Gaelic.
Colin Nicholson: Lecturer in English at Edinburgh University.
Kole Omotoso: Nigerian novelist, journalist.
Shaheed Quaderi: Bengali poet.
Jenny Robertson: Poet, playwright and author of children's books. Lives in Edinburgh.
John Robertson: b. Dundee, 1951, Fellow in History, St Hugh's College, Oxford. Author The Scottish Enlightenment and the Militia Issue, published by John Donald.
Rebecca Scott: Member, Hamilton Writers' Workshop - began writing three years ago once the four children had grown up!
Harry Smart: Consultant Editor, What Micro?. Criticism & Public Rationality Published Routledge, and first book of poems (Faber) both 1991.
Gillean Somerville: Lives in Edinburgh with Moroccan husband; stories and articles; co-editor of Sleeping with Monsters (Polygon).
Eunice de Souza: b.1940, teaches at St Xavier's College, Bombay. A new collection of poetry, Ways of Belonging, recently published by Polygon.
Charles Stephens: Writer on literature & visual art. Working on collection of essays on literature, music & visual arts in Europe since 1890.
Raymond Tong: Worked 20 years for Overseas Education Service and the British Council in Africa, Middle East, India and S. America.